The Watts History of Science Library

A HISTORY OF
THE THEORIES OF RAIN
AND OTHER FORMS OF PRECIPITATION

A HISTORY OF THE
THEORIES OF RAIN
AND OTHER FORMS OF PRECIPITATION

W. E. KNOWLES MIDDLETON
D.Sc., F.R.S.C.

Franklin Watts, Inc.
575 Lexington Avenue, New York, N.Y. 10022

PRINTED IN THE U.S.A.
BY MOFFA PRESS

Contents

Preface

The idea of writing a history of the theories of rain occurred to me when I was busy with my *The history of the barometer*. Although that work is strictly confined to the barometer as an instrument, I naturally came upon many articles on the interpretation of the changes in its indications – variations that in the seventeenth-century seemed contrary to all common sense. When the former book was completed I resolved to study this literature, and quickly realized that the story of the interpretation of the variations of the barometer was only a part of a very interesting subject.

The history of meteorology has had less attention, I imagine, than that of any other scientific discipline of comparable scope. This is almost certainly true of the current explosion of interest in the history of science and technology. As a striking example, consider the excellent *Histoire de la science* (Maurice Daumas, ed.) published in 1957 as part of the *Encylopédie de la Pléiade*. In the 1703 text pages of this work the admirable index is able to direct us to only two paragraphs dealing with meteorology, and of these one is devoted to Lucius Annaeus Seneca! Nor are very many scholarly papers being written on the subject; a recent survey (*Isis* 55 (1964), 132) of six of the leading journals in the History of Science for the period 1959–1963 revealed only one article on the history of meteorology out of 705 published during the five years in question. There would seem to be room for a work such as the present book.

I have attempted to carry the history of the theories of the hydrometeors up to about 1914. After the first world war the subject changed drastically, partly because of the great increase in our ability to make measurements in the upper air, and partly by the rapid development of the study of clouds as a branch of applied

vii

physics. The latter has been dealt with in a masterly fashion by Professor B. J. Mason (*The physics of clouds*, Oxford, 1957). The history of the former has yet to be written.

As far as possible I have used primary sources. Unless otherwise noted, translations from other languages are my own. In quoting from early printed works in English, I have preserved the spelling but removed the meaningless capitals and italics of which seventeenth- and eighteenth-century printers were so fond. The dates of the birth and death of most of the people mentioned in the text will be found in the index, which has also been provided with extensive cross-references.

I wish to thank Dr A. C. Crombie for reading Chapter One in draft form, Dr W. A. Smeaton for reading Chapter Six, and Mr D. Chilton for reading the entire draft. Each of these gentlemen made excellent suggestions; but the responsibility for the result remains entirely my own. I also wish to acknowledge the help of my old friend Stephen K. Marshall in translating a passage from Isidore of Seville.

Much of Chapter Three closely follows a paper read to the British Society for the History of Science in January, 1965.

I am grateful to the publishers of *Annals of science* for permission to reprint, from an article published there, some of Chapter Six; to Penguin Books, Ltd, for the quotation from Professor Farrington's *Greek Science*; to the Harvard University Press and William Heinemann for passages from the Loeb translation of Aristotle; and to the Cambridge University Press for the quotation from Sir Napier Shaw. The epigraph to the first chapter is from *The complete plays of Aristophanes* edited by Moses Hadas, Copyright © 1962, by Bantam Books, Inc., and reprinted by permission of the publisher.

My wife deserves more thanks than can possibly be given for typing the entire manuscript both in draft and in its final form, for helping with proofs and index, and for continual encouragement.

Chapter One

FROM THE EARLIEST TIMES TO THE INVENTION OF THE BAROMETER

> *Strepsiades: Tell me, do you think Zeus always rains
>   new water down*
> *Or does the sun draw the old up to be re-used?*
> *Amynias: I don't know and I don't care.*
> *Strepsiades: How do you expect to get your money if you
>   know nothing*
> *Of meteorology?*

Aristophanes, CLOUDS, trans.
Moses Hadas, New York,
Bantam Books, 1962, p. 136.

1. INTRODUCTION

Rain and snow, dew and frost and hail, the watery phenomena of the atmosphere have been of great concern to man from the distant time when he took shelter in caves, until the present day when the farmer, the engineer and the picnicker examine the sky or the weather forecast with their various concerns anxiously in mind. For many thousands of years man's interest in the hydrometeors was simply in their occurrence and their amount, apart from occasions of wonder at an unusually intense precipitation or its effects. It is still so for many of us. But sooner or later someone was bound to ask how, and also, no doubt, why it rained. The answer to the second question was at first easy: it rained in order to give him water for himself and his wife and his children, his animals and his crops. Much later he realized that his rivers, too, depended on rain for their flow. By this time the question how? was being asked and being given more-or-less cogent answers. As these answers became more probable, the question why? came to have less and less meaning, and finally none at all; it is so in the development of every science.

I

Probably everything written about the hydrometeors before the seventeenth century ought to be classified as speculation rather than theory. Nevertheless the mental constructions made in antiquity were at least founded on the observation of nature, though often very superficial observation, and I make no apology for devoting a few pages to them, even without the excuse that they formed a basis for more recent theories. For the truth is that they did not. The 'natural philosophers' of the seventeenth century could have started just where they did, even if there had been nothing whatever written about the hydrometeors in ancient times.

2. THE ANCIENT HEBREWS

Rain was of course extremely important to the inhabitants of Asia Minor, even though it is almost certain that the climate was somewhat moister in biblical times than at the present day. Most of the many references to rain in the Old Testament emphasize how welcome it was. But it is hard to find any indication of what, if anything, the Hebrews thought to be the physical cause of rain. There is a passage in the book of Amos which indicates some vague understanding of the hydrological cycle:

> Seek him . . . that calleth for the waters of the sea, and poureth them out upon the face of the earth; the Lord is his name.[1]

The prophet Amos lived in the eighth century B.C., but it is very probable that many passages in the book were inserted much later,[2] and this may be one of them. If not, it is a most interesting passage.

In a climate like that of Asia Minor, dew may be comparable with rain as a source of moisture in some seasons, and there are a number of appreciative references to it. It usually *falls*,[3] sometimes from the clouds,[4] a reference which might indicate careless observation. One should not make too much of such a passage as that of *Deuteronomy* XXXII, 2:

> My doctrine shall drop as the rain, my speech shall distil as the dew, as the small rain upon the tender herb, and as the showers upon the grass,

[1] *Amos* V, 8. See also p. 13 below.   [2] *Ency. Brit.*, 11th ed., *s.v.* 'Amos'.
[3] *2 Samuel* XVII, 12; *Deuteronomy* XXXIII, 28.   [4] *Proverbs* III, 20.

2

(how pleasant to say 'small rain' instead of 'drizzle'), but it is interesting to compare the following:

> . . . the Lord God had not caused it to rain upon the earth, and there was not a man to till the ground. But there went up a mist from the earth, and watered the whole face of the ground.[5]

It may just be possible that about the fifth century B.C. someone in Palestine had at least as clear an understanding of this prevalent phenomenon as anyone else before A.D. 1750. Nevertheless, such speculations are not very profitable, for the Bible is a great human document and not a textbook of physics, and the genius of the ancient Hebrews is in much better accord with the stupendous teleology of the thirty-eighth chapter of *Job*, which it will do no meteorologist any harm to read, whatever his feelings about such matters.

3. THE ANCIENT GREEKS AND ROMANS[6]

It is astonishing that the Greeks and the Hebrews, almost neighbours at the eastern end of the Mediterranean, should have differed so completely in their attitudes to the universe around them, and indeed to almost everything else. While the Hebrews seem to have been content to marvel at Nature, the Greeks began at a very early period to classify and to form systems. These were of course based on their observations of natural phenomena; but it was not long before there arose a predilection for logical completeness which, in the hands of a genius like Aristotle, seemed to render further observation superfluous and bedevilled the progress of physical science for about two thousand years.

The term *meteora* was in use by the time of Homer (eighth century B.C.) to denote the processes that took place in all the 'upper part' of the world, above the surface of the earth. Meteorology thus included astronomy, until Aristotle separated the two subjects. 'For the early physicists,' wrote Gilbert, 'meteorology formed the most

---

[5] *Genesis* II, 5–6.
[6] I have taken much of the material in this section from the extremely valuable and erudite work of Otto Gilbert, *Die meteorologischen Theorien des Greichischen Altertums*, Leipzig, 1907.

real and significant part of natural science.'[7] Indeed, to study it they had only to lift their eyes from their tablets.

In order to understand the ancient meteorological theories at all, we must pay some attention to the doctrine of the four elements and the ideas of the time regarding heat and cold. The four elements were fire, air, water, and earth. It is very difficult for a twentieth-century reader to understand just what was meant by this. We must not think of these elements as distinct substances, as we think of elements in present-day chemistry; they were rather principles; fire was not actual flame, but the principle of combustion; water, in a sense, the principle of fluidity and earth that of solidity. In Homer's time water and earth were the elements out of which the human body was considered to be made. The upper world was divided into air and aether, the former nearer the earth and the latter at greater heights. The aether seems at first to have been rather a region of space than an element, but with Homer it became a shining substance, fire. Air could condense or become thicker and turn to fog or cloud, and the element air was whatever filled the region immediately above the earth.

The Ionian physicists of the sixth century B.C. did not believe that the four elements were separate and unalterable in amount, but rather that they could be transformed into one another almost at will. Thales of Miletus, indeed, thought that all the elements came originally from water. The processes of inter-conversion were rarefaction and condensation, and these depended on heat and cold; but the elements could change into one-another only in the order:

$$\text{Fire} \leftrightarrow \text{air} \leftrightarrow \text{water} \leftrightarrow \text{earth}.$$

Earth, for example, could not change directly into air, or vice versa, but only through the state of water. According to Anaximenes, air might condense first to cloud, then to water, then to earth, and finally to stone.

From our present standpoint it is interesting to speculate, as Gilbert does,[8] that the Ionian philosophers deduced their theory of the interconvertibility of the elements from their interpretation of

---

[7] Gilbert, *Die meteorologischen Theorien*, p. 5. [8] Gilbert, p. 63.

common observations, such as a cloud over a large fire, and its subsequent disappearance; the falling of rain from clouds, and the visible breath of animals on cold days. They noted that the heat of the sun caused the evaporation of liquid water, and perhaps concluded from such an observation that the element fire plays a primary role in natural processes, and is different from the other elements in this respect. Earth, water and air are states of matter, but fire is a motive power or a creative force which changes matter from one form to the other.

It should be emphasized that the Ionians were not content merely to observe the world and describe what they saw. They wanted to 'explain' it, that is to say to fit it into a logical system of thought. 'In order to explain the phenomena of the senses,' says Farrington,

> they had had to invent a system of abstract ideas. Earth and water, it is true, might seem names for things seen and felt, but even these terms pass over into the more general ideas of solid and liquid; that is to say, they tend to become abstract terms. Still more clearly abstract are such ideas as the Indeterminate, or Condensation and Rarefaction, or Tension. The terms may, indeed, be taken from everyday life, but, as used by the philosophers, they become names of concepts invited [sic] to explain percepts. The distinction between the mind and the senses begins to appear.[9]

The ideas of the Eleatic school in the next century do not differ very greatly from those of the Ionians as far as the elements are concerned. To Empedocles of Akragas the four elements, which were of equal importance and existed in equal quantity, could not themselves be altered, but could mix together. They were made of very small particles, from combinations of which every substance arose. The forces of Nature that performed these changes were love and hate, which seems to leave little room for a theory of heat or cold; but it is probable that Empedocles associated heat with fire, dryness with air, cold with water, and moistness with earth.

We could spend many pages on the various Greek writers and their ideas about the four elements, though they all seem to have

[9] Benjamin Farrington, *Greek Science*, Penguin Books, 2 vols., 1944 and 1949, vol. I, p. 50.

agreed that in some way or other the elements were inter-convertible. This idea had inescapable consequences in the meteorological theories of Aristotle.

Some of these theories are contained in the first three books of the *Meteorologica*.[10] It has been mentioned that Aristotle was the first to separate meteorology and astronomy, though his meteorology includes all of what would now be called geophysics, and deals with all regions lower than the moon, in which regions, he believed, are found comets and the milky way. We shall confine ourselves as far as possible to his theories of the hydrometeors.

In the first place we must note that Aristotle refines and makes much more systematic the doctrine of the four elements. These are produced by combinations of two of the *primary qualities* heat, cold, dryness, and moistness, as follows:

$$
\begin{aligned}
\text{Hot} + \text{dry} &= \text{fire} \\
\text{Hot} + \text{wet} &= \text{air} \\
\text{Cold} + \text{wet} &= \text{water} \\
\text{Cold} + \text{dry} &= \text{earth}
\end{aligned}
$$

Each of the elements has its own natural position; thus fire always tends to rise to the top, earth to go to the bottom, water to rise above earth, air above water but below fire. All the four elements 'are transformable one into another, and ... each is potentially latent in the others'.[11]

Now what is air? This seems to depend on where it is.

> ... we must understand that of what we call air the part which immediately surrounds the earth is moist and hot because it is vaporous and contains exhalations from the earth, but that the part above this is hot and dry. For vapour is naturally moist and cold and exhalation hot and dry:[12] and vapour is potentially like water, exhalation like fire.[13]

[10] The most convenient edition for English-speaking students is in the Loeb Classical Library, no. 397, London and Cambridge, Mass., 1952, where it is translated, with useful notes, by H. D. P. Lee.

[11] *Meteorologica, ed. cit.*, Book I, chap. 3.

[12] This distinction between vapours and exhalations was to bedevil meteorological theory long after Aristotelianism in the strict sense had gone out of fashion.

[13] *Meteorologica*, I, 3.

The fact that the upper air is potentially like fire explains why clouds do not form above the level of the highest mountains.

Aristotle's speculations about precipitation are seen to follow from his doctrine of the elements, the qualities that make them up, and their interconvertibility, combined with what may seem to us a very arbitrary interpretation of simple observations. Like his predecessors he accepted the conversion of air into water; but while the Ionian physicists considered clouds as a thickened form of air, standing between air and water in their properties, Aristotle appears to know that clouds are water:

> The efficient, controlling and first cause is the circle of the sun's revolution . . . . The earth is at rest, and the moisture about it is evaporated by the sun's rays and the other heat from above and rises upwards; but when the heat which caused it to rise leaves it . . . the vapour cools and condenses again as a result of the loss of heat and the height and turns from air into water: and having become water falls again onto the earth. The exhalation from water is vapour; the formation of water from air produces cloud. Mist is the residue of the condensation of air into water, and is therefore a sign of fine weather rather than of rain . . .[14]

We may note that there is no clear distinction between air and vapour, except that the latter comes from the evaporation of water. There is, it is interesting to note in the same chapter, a distinction between drizzle and rain. Dew and frost result from moisture that has evaporated during the day but does not rise far; for, he has noted, they do not form on mountains. Both occur only in clear, calm weather.[15]

Aristotle's theory of the formation of rain from cloud cannot be deduced in its entirety from the *Meteorology*, as Gilbert has pointed out.[16] Parts of it are in the *Physics* and in *On the Heavens*,[17] and it is difficult to put together a consistent account. Briefly it may be summarized as follows: The formation of rain is dependent on the cooling of the air, as we have seen. The heat in the clouds, because it is the nature of heat to rise, tries to ascend and get free from them.

[14] *Ibid.*, I, 9.   [15] *Ibid.*, I, 10.   [16] Gilbert, p. 497.
[17] Both are available in translation in the Loeb collection.

7

The cold in the vapour (*atmis*) struggles with this heat, and having driven it away, presses the particles of the cloud closer together. This restores to the *atmis* the true nature of the element water, which had been temporarily obscured by the heat. Water naturally moves downwards, so that the turning of cloud into rain is entirely normal and in accordance with natural law.

Rain, snow and hail fall from the clouds, dew and frost form near the surface of the earth. Aristotle notes that there is no terrestrial analogue to hail. The difference between rain and dew, and between snow and frost, is purely quantitative, depending on the amount of vapour available and the length of time it has been accumulating.[18] Hail presented special problems to Aristotle, as it has to many others from that day to this. As hail is ice, it is surprising that it occurs least often in winter. And how does the necessary water remain suspended in the air?[19] Aristotle's answers to these questions are examples of the weakness of his scientific method. He can see that minute drops of water can coalesce to form rain; but frozen drops cannot coalesce, so that drops of the requisite size must have been suspended in the air before they froze. Anaxagoras, he says, thought that hail is produced when a cloud is forced upwards into a region of low temperature, but Aristotle believes that large hailstones are formed near the ground by an intense cause of freezing. He notes that the large stones are not spherical, and adduces this as a proof that they have frozen near the ground, 'for stones which fall farther are worn down in the course of their fall and so become round in shape and smaller in size'.[20]

But how does the freezing take place? Hot and cold have a mutual reaction[21] on one another, which is why caves are cold in summer and warm in winter. We must suppose that the same reaction takes place in the air,

> so that in warmer seasons the cold is concentrated within by the surrounding heat. This sometimes causes a rapid formation of water from

---

[18] *Meteorologica*, I, 11   [19] *Ibid.*, I, 12.   [20] *Ibid.*, I, 12.

[21] This is Lee's translation in this particular context of the awkward word *antiperistasis*, which is always bobbing up in classical and medieval physics. Lee justifies his interpretation in a long footnote, *Meteorologica*, pp. 82–3.

8

cloud. And for this reason you get larger raindrops on warm days than in winter and more violent rainfall – rainfall is said to be more violent when it is heavier, and a heavier rainfall is caused by rapidity of condensation. (The process is just the opposite of what Anaxagoras says it is. He says it takes place when a cloud rises into the cold air: we say it takes place when a cloud descends into the warm air and is most violent when the cloud descends farthest.) Sometimes, on the other hand, the cold is even more concentrated within by the heat outside it, and freezes the water which it has produced, so forming hail. This happens when the water freezes before it has time to fall.

. . . The nearer the earth and the more intense the freezing, the more violent the rainfall and the larger the drops or the hailstones because of the shortness of their fall . . .[22]

One would think that a simple examination of a large hailstone would have caused Aristotle to doubt this strange explanation. But it may be doubted whether he was at all interested in making any observations or experiments that would test his 'theory'. He disposes of Anaxagoras, who was much more nearly right, by simply contradicting him.

The atomists had theories of hail. Epicurus, seeing that it is always connected with storms, ascribed a hailstone to the surrounding of a small complex of water atoms by a larger mass of wind atoms. The generally rounded forms of hailstones were felt to support this theory.[23] In this connection it is interesting that Aristotle and later classical writers absolutely denied that winds were air in motion, but thought they were dry exhalations from the earth. Although earlier philosophers – e.g. Hippocrates and Anaximander – had believed that winds were moving air, Aristotle[24] discarded their ideas with the utmost contempt, saying that 'the unscientific views of ordinary people (hoi polloi) are preferable to scientific theories of this sort'.

We must leave Aristotle with a brief reference to his beliefs regarding the origin of rivers. These ideas were a logical consequence of the doctrine of the interconvertibility of the elements. Since air can change to water, and vice versa, above ground, it is illogical to

[22] Ibid., I, 12.   [23] Gilbert, Die meteorologischen Theorien, pp. 506–7.
[24] Meteorologica, I, 13.

assume that this does not happen in the pores of the earth. The mountains, in which streams arise, act like sponges and soak up the air. We need not neglect the rainfall, but Aristotle, who lived on the relatively dry Mediterranean coast, believed that there was not nearly enough of it. The importance of rain in this connection was minimized by the Stoics, to whom the world was a living organism, water its blood. But it seems likely that Aristotle's immediate successor Theophrastus returned to a meteorological explanation of the origin of streams.[25] The question was still being debated in the eighteenth century.

No significant progress in meteorology was made in classical antiquity after the time of Aristotle. The transfer of the centre of culture to Alexandria and the rise of Rome had the final result of standardizing nearly every field of knowledge in handbooks, thus, as William H. Stahl has recently argued, drying up research.[26] Lucius Annaeus Seneca, and Gaius Plinius Secundus, known as Pliny the Elder, are the chief of these handbook writers. Pliny's *Natural History*[27] is an enormous compilation that claims to record 20,000 facts, many if not most of them travellers' tales and superstitions. In the meteorological part of this work there is nothing original. Seneca's *Natural Questions*[28] is much shorter but equally derivative. It differs from Aristotle's *Meteorology* in one interesting point: Seneca defines wind as air in motion,[29] but as to how it is produced, he says the earth emits great quantities of air from its interior, and draws the amusing parallel of human eructations.[30] But this is only one cause; the atmosphere possesses an inherent capacity for movement, not derived from any external source.

The importance of Pliny and Seneca is that they helped to transmit Greek science, at least in an imperfect version, to the early Middle Ages, which might otherwise have been entirely ignorant of it.

[25] See Gilbert, pp. 425–7. [26] *Roman Science*, Madison, Wis., 1962.
[27] In the translation by H. Rackham and W. H. S. Jones, London, 1938–63, 10 vols., the meteorology is in Vol. I (tr. Rackham, 1938).
[28] *Physical Science in the time of Nero, being a translation of the* Quaestiones naturales *of Seneca*, by John Clarke . . . with notes . . . by Sir Archibald Geikie. London, 1910.
[29] Book V, ch. I. [30] Book V, ch. 4.

All in all, classical meteorology did not get very far. In large measure this was due to the tremendous reputation of the world-system devised by Aristotle.[31] We must not blame him for this; he had undoubtedly created his magnificent synthesis without any feeling that it might be falsifiable by experiment or even by observation. Such was its power that, re-introduced to the West in the twelfth century, it continued to rule the minds of nearly all the investigators of nature up to the time of Galileo, who was born almost nineteen hundred years after Aristotle's death.

4. THE NEXT FIFTEEN CENTURIES

The reader may well be surprised to find such a long period as a millenium and a half bundled unceremoniously into the end of a chapter, especially in view of the rehabilitation of the later Middle Ages which has been going on in recent years.[32] But somehow it seems that in spite of a number of remarkable advances, especially in mechanics and in optics, the science of meteorology failed to make any significant progress in the Christian lands. This is not to say that there was no interest in the subject; indeed Hellmann remarked on the extent of this interest in reprinting large extracts from twenty-six works bearing on meteorology between the seventh and four-teenth centuries.[33] But when one comes to read what was written, one finds little but dreary variations on what remained of the meteorology of Aristotle and the later Greeks, as passed on in the handbooks of Pliny and Seneca. I shall therefore confine myself to the mention of a few examples, trying to pick up any crumbs of originality that may be lying about. Of course there remains the possibility that in some of the very large number of manuscripts so far unpublished, something quite different might be found.

[31] See, for example, E. J. Dijksterhuis, *The mechanization of the world picture*, trans. C. Dikshoorn. Oxford, the Clarendon Press, 1961, pp. 69–72, also S. Sambursky, *The physical world of the Greeks*, London, Routledge, 1963, Chapter IV.

[32] See, for example, A. C. Crombie, *Medieval and early modern science*, 2nd ed., revised; Garden City, N.Y., Doubleday & Co., 1959. 2 vol.

[33] Gustav Hellmann, 'Denkmäler mittelalterlicher Meteorologie.' *Neudrücke von Schriften und Karten über Meteorologie und Erdmagnetismus*, whole vol. XV, Berlin, 1904.

While the decline of ancient science had begun well before the beginning of the Christian era, and so cannot be blamed on Christianity, there is no doubt that the early revival of scientific activity in Europe was rendered impossible by the philosophical position of the early Church.[34] The Church claimed complete control of the human spirit; man, once 'a little lower than the angels', was now a helpless creature utterly dependent on God for his knowledge as well as for his daily bread. The sterner Fathers such as Tertullian maintained that all investigation of, or speculation about the universe was useless and indeed impious, for the truth about everything had been revealed. The greater ones, like Augustine, saw that Nature was the work of God and did not quite condemn its investigation, but firmly believed in the supreme authority of Scripture. As a result of this, those who wrote about science in the first millenium were chiefly interested in using it to illustrate and interpret Holy Writ. As a fairly typical example of this sort of writing, I have attempted a translation of the opening of an article 'On Clouds' in a short compendium of cosmology entitled *On the nature of things*, By Isidore, Bishop of Seville:[35]

We may read in the book of *Job* that the air is condensed and becomes visible when it is gathered together. For he says, 'Suddenly the air is pressed into clouds, and the passing wind drives them away.'[36] And Vergil says, 'The winds arise and the air is condensed into clouds.'[37] The clouds are to be understood as holy evangelists, who pour the rain of the divine word on those who believe. For the air itself, empty and thin, signifies the empty and wandering minds of men, and then, thickened and turned into clouds, typifies the confirmation in the Faith of minds chosen from among the empty vanity of the unfaithful. And just as rainy clouds are made from the empty air, so the holy evangelists are gathered to the Faith from the vanity of this world.

[34] For a detailed study of the patristic writings touching on meteorology, see Immanuel Hoffmann, *Münchener Geogr. Studien* 22 (1907), 1–96. In his conclusion he states flatly that 'progress in meteorological knowledge is nowhere to be recognized' (p. 93), although his studies cover the first nine centuries.

[35] Hellmann, *Denkmäler*, p. 3–4. Also in Migne, *Patrologia Latina*, vol. 83, col. 1005.

[36] Migne says *Job* XXXVII, 21; but only the last phrase is recognizable in the Authorized Version.

[37] *Aeneid*, V, 20.

In the next article, 'On Rain', after quoting the passage from *Amos* to which we have already referred, and repeating some ideas out of Seneca, Isidore likens rain to the eloquence of the apostles, dropping on men the fertility of doctrine. Similarly hail typifies the hardness of perfidy;

> snow signifies unbelievers, very cold and lazy, their minds depressed in the most extreme torpor; or in another interpretation men growing cold in love, who, even if white by virtue of the purification of baptism, do not glow with the spirit of charity.

When we consider that Isidore was the greatest of western medieval encyclopaedists, it will be clear that in such an intellectual environment progress was unlikely. Even Augustine could believe that God permitted demons to affect the weather.[38] So, a thousand years later, could Dante.[39] Brehaut has put the matter in a nutshell:

> . . . the attitude of Isidore and his time is exactly opposite to ours. To him the supernatural world was the demonstrable and ordered one. Its phenomena, or what were supposed to be such, were accepted as valid, while no importance was attached to evidence offered by the senses as to the material [world].[40]

Medieval thinkers were convinced of the unity of the world; they could not understand that there could be more than one way of looking at the universe. A particular difficulty, as Wright[41] noted, lay in the 'waters above the firmament' (Genesis I, 6–7). This very un-Aristotelian position for water was highly embarrassing.

We may record that it is possible to divide the writers on meteorology of this period into two groups, according to their beliefs about the nature of wind. Some of Aristotle's successors had been unable to swallow his categorical assertion that wind was not air in motion; this minority opinion had been transmitted by Seneca.

[38] See Hoffmann, *Münchener Geogr. Studien*, 22 (1907), 88.

[39] *Purgatorio*, V, 112–14.

[40] E. Brehaut, *An encyclopaedist of the Dark Ages: Isidore of Seville*. New York, 1912, (Studies in History, Economics and Public Law, Columbia Univ., 48 (1912), 1–274), p. 67.

[41] Thomas Wright, *Popular treatises on science written during the Middle Ages, in Anglo-Saxon, Anglo-Norman, and English*. London, 1841, p. 58.

With the exception of Philoponos,[42] the opinions of the various writers therefore depended on whether they had derived their ideas from him or from Pliny. Most of them followed Seneca.

It will be noted that ancient Greek science was known to the western world at this time only through the Roman handbook writers. What remained of the original books was conserved in the east, and came into the hands of the Moslem Arabs, and from the seventh to the twelfth century the Arabs made excellent use of them, especially in mathematics, optics, and theoretical astronomy. But again, meteorology seems to have made relatively little progress, though of course many manuscripts are still in need of study.

One interesting writer who should claim our attention for a moment is Iyyūbh, or Job of Edessa. In 817 he wrote a *Book of Treasures*, a sort of small encyclopaedia of science.[43] It is plain that Iyyūbh has read his Aristotle, but he is not hypnotized by him. Wind has become moving air, with no nonsense about dry exhalations. It moves the clouds, he says, 'collects them and condenses them by bringing them closely together, and also dispels them and gives rise to fine weather'.[44] He had the rather strange idea that when it rains the inner parts of the clouds condense to continuous liquid water and burst out in a great stream, which breaks up into raindrops while falling. And of course he had a teleological explanation of the hydrometeors: they were made by a wise God for the use of mankind, with the exception of hail, which is to chastise us for our evil ways.

A much more important book was the encyclopaedia written in the tenth century by a secret society of Basra, usually called 'The Brethren of Purity'.[45] Their meteorology shows a distinct advance over that of the Greeks. They showed, for example, how the air is

---

[42] On Philoponos, see George Sarton, *Introduction to the history of science*, Vol. I, Washington 1927, p. 421–2.

[43] *Encyclopaedia of philosophical and natural sciences, as taught at Baghdad about A.D. 817, or, Book of Treasures*. Syriac text edited and translated with a critical apparatus by A. Mingana. Cambridge, Heffer, 1935.

[44] *Ibid.*, p. 193.

[45] Hellmann (*Denkmäler*, pp. 23–41) has published a German translation of the meteorological part of this. On the Brethren, see Sarton, *Introduction*, I, 660–1.

warmed from the ground up, and that this depends on the elevation of the sun. They noted the daily variation of temperature, and the influence of mountains on precipitation. They recognized that the wind is air in motion, and thought that it was produced by the rising of vapour from the sea and heated exhalations from the land warmed by the sun; an explanation which suggests close observation of land-and-sea breezes.

These same rising vapours are the material of cloud, rain, dew, hoar-frost, fog, drizzle, thunder, lightning, and hail. The Brethren seem to have been vaguely aware of the role of cooling in producing cloud and rain, but could not quite rid themselves of the classical idea of clouds being compressed by the winds. They had a neat explanation of dew:

If the rise of this fresh vapour happens during the night, while the air is very cold, the vapour is prevented from rising in the air, and is allowed to condense gradually near the surface of the earth . . .

This was not really improved on until the eighteenth century. But they were even better about rain:

If the air is warm, these vapours rise to a great height, and the clouds collect one above the other stepwise, as is observed in spring and autumn. It is as if they were mountains of combed cotton, one over another. But if cold from the zone of ice comes in from above, the vapours collect and become water; then their parts are pressed together, and they become drops, increase in weight and fall from the upper region of the cloud down through its mass. These little drops unite with one another until, if they come out of the lower boundary of the cloud, they are large drops of rain. If they meet great cold on their way, they freeze together and become hail before they reach the ground. In consequence, those that come from the upper part of the cloud will be hail, but those from the lower boundary of the cloud will be rain mixed with hail.

They go on to compare the process with the distillation of rose-water, vinegar, and so on, and with the collection of drops of water on the ceilings of bath-houses from the rising steam.

So the lower boundary of the region of icy cold, and the high mountains round about the sea[46] confine the two rising streams of vapour

[46] It is not quite easy to see the Persian Gulf in this.

from which clouds and rain come; they scatter them and take them away, just like the walls and roofs of bath-houses.

The reader will agree that this is no pale imitation of Aristotle. As far as my reading extends, I have found no more intelligible or perspicacious interpretation of weather before the invention of the barometer.

It is also refreshingly free from theology. Something of this separation of theology and science got into western writings too, just before the works of Aristotle were made available in Latin translation. The best example, at least in meteorology, is Guillaume de Conches,[47] who really did his best to give purely physical explanations of natural phenomena, and got into a little trouble with his ecclesiastical superiors as a result. His meteorological speculations, which have been published by Hellmann,[48] bear some resemblance to those of the Brethren of Purity, but they contain less observation and more thought. Whence comes the rain? asks William; and he answers:

> Rain has . . . various causes. For sometimes thick and wet steam (*fumus*) evaporates, and as it ascends, minute droplets become entangled in it. When these have thus become larger and heavier, they fall, and rain occurs. But sometimes air is thickened on account of the coldness of the land and the water, and turns into a watery substance which, dried because of the heat of the sun, like ice by fire, falls down in very small particles. Sometimes it happens that the sun, in order to feed its heat, attracts moisture, and the more liquid part of this turns into a fiery substance. This falls down more heavily, when after a very great heat we see a flood of rain. But there is some question about this.[49]

Indeed there might be.

This happy independence of science came to a quick end after the classical Greek authors were rediscovered by the West. This happened in the last half of the twelfth century, and by the middle of the thirteenth the great intellects of Thomas Aquinas and Albert

---

[47] See Sarton, *Introduction*, II, 197–9; also E. J. Dijksterhuis, *The mechanization of the world picture*, trans. C. Dikshoorn, Oxford, Clarendon Press, 1961, pp. 120–3.

[48] *Denkmäler*, pp. 42–54 and 69–75.

[49] Translated from Hellmann, *Denkmäler*, p. 70.

the Great had succeeded in the unlikely task of incorporating the doctrines of Aristotle into those of the Church. This was made possible because of the extent and scope of the logical system bequeathed to them by Aristotle, and it is to this great impressiveness that its extraordinary longevity must be ascribed.

Some of the parts of physics that had little bearing on theology – especially mechanics and optics – made important advances in the next three hundred years. Meteorology seems to have been less fortunate. One of the results of the Aristotelian revival, needless to say, was to restore his ideas about the wind. Albert the Great himself, in his commentary on the *Meteorologica*, insists at length that winds are not moving air.[50] Albert also wrote another meteorological work *De passionibus aëris*,[51] which seems to have a good deal of observation in it.

While the casting of horoscopes was discouraged, the belief in the physical influence of the stars was not, and of course nothing could be more readily ascribed to their configurations than the weather. Elaborate books on astro-meteorology continued to be published until late in the eighteenth century, one of the most popular having its third edition in 1797.[52] Between about 1300 and 1650, however, they shared the field with straight commentaries on Aristotle's *Meteorologica*, which appeared in large numbers among the hundreds devoted to his other works. We need not consider them further. Naturally there were occasional aberrations, more interesting than the commentaries though not necessarily more important, such as Mizauld's *Mirror of the air*.[53] Why, he asks, are raindrops round? Because the corners get rubbed off as they fall side by side. Besides, the round shape is a good one for overcoming the resistance of the air. But there is another reason, thoroughly *seizième siècle*:

[50] Albert the Great, *De meteoris libri IV*, Book III, part I, chap. vii–ix.

[51] Hellmann, *Denkmäler*, pp. 105 ff., prints the introduction and table of contents of this.

[52] Giuseppe Toaldo, *Della vera influenza degli astri sulle stagioni e mutazioni di tempo*. Padova, 1770.

[53] Antoine Mizauld, *Le Mirouer de l'air, autrement dict meteorologie, ou bien petit commentaire des choses de l'air*, Paris, 1548.

Or else because the parts of the world, let them be as small as you will, are obliged to represent the round image of the universe, and so give some sort of example of the entire terrestrial machine in the form of a pattern and design, as far as possible proportioned and similar to it.[54]

On the next page we hear that large raindrops, which at any rate come from the warmer clouds, seem warm because they fall very fast and acquire heat in doing so. The speed of large raindrops seems to have impressed people; in the next century we are told in all seriousness that '. . . in the land of Mexico the raindrops fall with such violence that they are said to kill men.[55]

This brings us to the seventeenth century and to Francis Bacon, whose *Historia ventorum* was published in London in 1622.[56] Alas! the great champion of experimental science seems to find it convenient to make frequent references to Pliny;[57] and we are told that winds are produced (1) from the exhalations of the earth, (2) from 'vapours' raised by the heat of the sun. Such vapours may turn into wind or into rain; moreover

> Windes do contract themselves into rain, . . . either being burthened by the burthen it selfe, when the vapours are copious, or by the contrary motions of windes, so they be calme and milde; or by the opposition of mountains and promontories which stop the violence of the windes, and by little and little turn them against themselves; or by extream colds, whereby they are condensed and thickened.[58]

If even Bacon could not persuade himself to admit that he did not know how rain is formed, there is no wonder that for two centuries and more the German universities emitted a constant stream of

[54] *Ibid.*, p. 11. '*Ou bien par ce que les parties du monde, tant petites soyent elles qu'on vouldra, s'efforcent representer la rond image de l'université, & donner exemple tel quel, de la totale machine mondaine, soubz quelque patron & esbauchement, autant que possible est à elle proportionné & semblable.*'

[55] J. Jonston, *Thaumatographia naturalis*, [etc.], 2nd ed., Amsterdam, 1633, p. 127.

[56] Translated into English in 1653 as *The naturall and experimentall history of winds* [etc.].

[57] *Cf.* E. G. R. Taylor, *Late Tudor and early Stuart geography, 1583–1650*, London 1934, p. 89: '. . . it can hardly be said that any English work of the early seventeenth century represented an advance on Pliny.'

[58] *The Naturall and experimental history of winds*, p. 101.

dissertations with the titles *De pluvia, De meteoris aqueis*, etc.[59] None of the few that I have examined are of any value.

We are now getting into the period of instrumental meteorology, and particularly of the use of the barometer. The ideas of René Descartes about rain might reasonably be discussed here, but they form only a small part of his ideas on the behaviour of water in the atmosphere, so that I shall use him to introduce the next chapter instead, in which I shall try to follow the progress of thought about the nature of water vapour and the way in which it is produced.

[59] With occasional variants like *Deus ex pluvia* (Gerhard Meier, Diss. Hamburg, 1697).

Chapter Two

SEVENTEENTH- AND EIGHTEENTH-CENTURY
IDEAS ABOUT WATER VAPOUR

Ben sai come nell'Aere si raccoglie
Quell' umido vapor, che in Acqua riede
Tosto che sale, dove 'l freddo il coglie.
—Dante, PURGATORIO, V, 109–11.

1. VAPOUR IS NOT AIR

The artificial division of the subject implied in the headings of this and the next two chapters must not be taken to mean that these lines of inquiry proceeded in isolation during the period in question. Indeed, two or even all three of them were often dealt with in the same book or article; but it seems clear that if this history is to be any more than a chronology, some attempt must be made to deal with them one at a time, even at the cost of many cross-references. Because water vapour is the raw material of all the hydrometeors, an understanding of its nature and properties had to be attained before even a general explanation of their formation could be expected. I shall therefore begin with a consideration of the various ideas about water vapour and its production, held between about 1637, when Descartes' *Les meteores*[1] appeared, and about 1770.

René Descartes was a very great philosopher who had a tremendous effect on the progress of science, even though nearly all his detailed explanations of natural phenomena have turned out to be wrong. His belief in the power of reason led him to make confident statements about the structure of matter, among many other things. He believed that all bodies are composed of particles of various shapes and sizes, though all of the same substance, surrounded and

[1] All references to Descartes will be to *Oeuvres*, Ed. Ch. Adam and Paul Tannery, 12 vol. and index, Paris, 1896–1911. *Les meteores* is in vol. 6 (1902), pp. 231–366.

kept apart by a different and extremely tenuous material, the 'subtle matter', also composed of particles of various sizes, always in motion, and completely filling the space between the larger particles of matter. There could be no empty space whatever. What we should now call the elastic and rheological properties of matter were to be accounted for by the shape and arrangement of its particles.

Water, in particular, was supposed by Descartes to be composed of long smooth eel-shaped particles which can easily be separated; but the particles of almost all others, even air, are very irregular in shape. Air and the light liquids differ from hard solids only in that the particles of the latter are close together and interlaced.

Heat is a manifestation of the motion of the subtle matter; the faster it moves, the higher the temperature. The freezing of water is due to the lessened agitation of the subtle matter, which can no longer keep the water-particles apart.

With this background, Descartes' explanation of the process of evaporation should present no difficulty:

> If you consider that the subtle matter in the pores of terrestrial bodies, being more strongly agitated at one time than at another either by the presence of the sun or for some other reason, also agitates the tiny parts of these bodies more strongly, you will easily understand that it can make those which are small enough, and which can be separated easily from their neighbours, break away here and there and fly into the air. This is not at all because of some particular inclination to rise, but only because they find no other place in which it is so easy to continue their movement. In the same way, the dust of a field flies up when it is merely disturbed and propelled by the feet of a passer-by. For though the grains of this dust are much larger and heavier than the small particles of which we are speaking, this does not stop them taking their course towards the sky . . . This should prevent us being astonished at the action of the sun, raising so high the little particles of matter of which vapours and exhalations are composed, seeing that it is extended over half the earth at every moment, and that it persists for entire days. But note that these particles which are thus raised into the air by the sun, ought mostly to have the shape that I have attributed to those of water, because there are no others that can be so easily separated from the bodies in which they are. It will be these alone that I particularly refer to as vapours, in order to distinguish them from

others of more irregular shape, to which I shall give the name of exhalations, because I know no better one.[2]

We must remember that at that time, and indeed much later, every substance with the properties of what we now call a gas was simply called 'air'. If it was transparent and apparently not there at all, it was air. Consequently it was quite natural to believe that water was transformed into air on evaporation, and indeed the recognition of water vapour as a separate and different substance was somewhat of an intellectual achievement. Descartes was quite clear about the difference, expressing it in terms of his hypothetical particles. The particles of water vapour were of the same slender figure as those of water, but were separated by much more of the subtle matter. 'And we should not doubt that the air often contains as much or more vapour when this is entirely invisible, as it does when it can be seen.'[3]

Otto von Guericke, the inventor of the air pump, whose experiments were done in 1656 or earlier,[4] also states clearly that moisture can enter the air and be again condensed into liquid water, but that air cannot be turned into water. The lower part of the atmosphere always contains invisible moisture, its amount depending on the weather.

> ... in summer ... we see that glasses and other wine vessels, brought up out of cold cellars, seem to sweat. The reason is that the air around the vessel is cooled by it, and so contracts, and in consequence releases its watery humour, which then adheres to the side of the vessel.[5]

It would seem that Guericke thought that the contraction of the air by cold squeezed out the water; but as we shall see in Chapter Three,[6] he also produced precipitation by the rarefaction of moist air.

By this time the transformation of water into vapour, and not into air, was becoming a familiar idea, used as a minor weapon by the enlightened against the rearguard of the Peripatetic army, in

---

[2] *Les meteores*, pp. 239–40.   [3] *Ibid.*, p. 246.

[4] He wrote about them to Caspar Schott, on 18 June 1656. See Schott, *Technica curiosa, sive mirabilia artis* [etc.], Nürnberg, 1664, pp. 24–25.

[5] Guericke, *Ottonis de Guericke Experimenta nova (ut vocantur) Magdeburgica de vacuo spatio primùm à R. P. Gaspare Schotto ... nunc vero ab ipso Autore perfectiùs edita, variisque aliis experimentis aucta* [etc.]. Amsterdam 1672, p. 89.

[6] See p. 45.

retreat under the attacks of Pascal and of Boyle. In 1681 Giuseppe del Papa, a professor at Pisa, even used the lines of Dante that I have placed at the head of this chapter as proof that water does not turn into air: 'The vapour, he says, turns back into water; this is as much as to say that water, first rarefied by heat, is condensed by cold, and returns to water; not, to be sure, that air is changed to water.'[7] As the whole thing turns on the word *vapor*, it is much more likely that Dante was just remembering something out of Aristotle.

2. THE RISE OF VAPOUR

The fact that vapour rises and remains in the air still bothered people, in spite of Descartes, whose metaphor of the dust kicked up from the field may possibly have engendered the reflection that the dust also comes down again. One explanation, greatly favoured for more than a century, was suggested in 1666 by a priest, Urbano d'Aviso.[8] He believed that vapour was 'little bubbles of water filled with fire . . . which ascend through the air as long as it is of greater specific gravity than they are; and when they arrive at a place where the air is equally light, they stop'. In 1688 Edmond Halley, apparently independently, gave a similar explanation to the Royal Society; he was not sure what if anything is inside the bubbles, but would not exclude the possibility that there may be 'a certain sort of matter whose *conatus* may be contrary to that of gravity: as is evident in vegetation, wherein the tendency of the sprouts is directly upwards or against the perpendicular'.[9]

It is fascinating to discover that only two years before Halley read his paper, a suggestion was published (also in the *Philosophical Transactions*) which, if applied to the atmosphere, would have provided the correct explanation.[10] In this paper, William Molyneux

[7] G. del Papa, *Della natura dell'vmido, e del secco, lettera all'illustrissimo Sig. Francesco Reddi*. Florence 1681, p. 141.

[8] Urbano d'Aviso, *Lettera al dottor G. B. Capponi*. Bologna, 1666, p. 79. Cited by I. Galli, *Mem. Accad. Nuovi Lincei* 27 (1909), 233, note.

[9] *Phil. Trans.* 17 (1693), 469.

[10] William Molyneux, 'A Discourse on this Problem; why Bodies dissolved in Menstrua specifically lighter than themselves, swim therein.' *Phil. Trans.* 16 (1686), 88–93.

discussed a suggestion made by his brother Thomas[11] regarding the reason why heavy bodies remain dissolved and suspended in liquids much lighter than themselves. Thomas Molyneux thought that the explanation was to be found in 'the internal motion of the parts of the liquor'.

> [The particles of the solute] being so very minute, are movable by the least force imaginable, and the action of the particles of the *menstruum*, is sufficient to drive the atomes of the dissolved solid body from place to place; and consequently, notwithstanding their gravity, they do not sink in the liquid lighter than themselves.[12]

William did not think this a necessary explanation, and preferred to believe that the particles of the solute were unable to separate the particles of the liquid, which tend to stick together. In a reply appended to the paper, Thomas asks whether the 'cause' advocated by William can get the heavy substance into solution in the first place, as his would. Here is a prevision of the molecular motion first demonstrated experimentally only in 1828.[13] Very little attention was paid to this paper, and of course nobody thought of applying it to the atmosphere, although Halley noted the apparent similarity between evaporation and the solution of solids in liquids. We shall return later to this last analogy.

Water vapour might rise in air if it were lighter than air. This obvious possibility appeared too absurd to be considered seriously until Sir Isaac Newton stated categorically that it was so, in the famous *omnibus* query 31 appended to the third English edition of his *Opticks* (1717):[14]

> And because the particles of permanent air are grosser, and arise from denser substances than those of vapours, thence it is that true air is more ponderous than vapour, and that a moist atmosphere is lighter than a dry one, quantity for quantity.[15]

This was too alarming a statement to be well received, even by Newton's eighteenth-century worshippers. I do not in fact recall any

[11] They were both Fellows of the Royal Society and men of much distinction.
[12] *Ibid.*, p. 88–89.   [13] Robert Brown, *Phil. Mag.*, N.S. 4 (1828), 161–73.
[14] Newton, *Opticks, or a treatise of the reflections, refractions, inflections and colours of light*. Reprinted 1952 by Dover Publications, Inc., New York.
[15] *Ed. cit.*, p. 396.

direct reference to it before 1770, and I can only assume that it must
have been ignored by common consent. It is doubly alarming,
because even if we accept the entirely unsupported idea – could it
have been an unconscious echo of Descartes? – that the particles of
air are individually the heavier, it did nothing to dispel the feeling,
ubiquitous then and long after, that in moist air some vapour is
added to the dry air already there, so that the mixture, or whatever
it was, must still be 'more ponderous'. This statement of Newton's
can only be explained as an authentic instance of genius having
intuitions far beyond experience; he would have worked
himself through the position taken by Daniel Bernouilli twenty
years later to the experimental verification of the last part of
the statement about 1780. His reasons were, as we know, quite
unsound.

At about this time, the success of Thomas Newcomen's 'atmospheric engine'[16] aroused interest in the properties of steam. In 1729
the physicist J. T. Desaguliers and the surveyor Henry Beighton
found, they supposed, that water in boiling is expanded 14,000
times when it produces 'a steam as strong (*i.e.* as elastick) as common
air'.[17] But when air is heated to the boiling point of water, (presumably from room temperature) says Desaguliers, it expands only to
about 5/3 its original volume. Therefore as 'the same degree of heat
rarefies vapour much more than air', vapour will rise. This seems to
be a *non sequitur*, but the paper is interesting because of the implied
assumption that the vapour from boiling water, and the invisible
vapour that rises from water at a lower temperature, are one and the
same thing, a view by no means commonly held at the time. The
trouble was that the former quickly became 'steam', and as quickly
dispersed again; it was not easy to recognize the region of invisible
vapour just over the boiling water.

Desaguliers's paper is also of interest because of an idea thrown
out rather casually as a 'Scholium', that

[16] *See* L. T. C. Rolt, *Thomas Newcomen. The prehistory of the steam engine.* Dawlish
and London, 1963.

[17] *Phil. Trans.* 36 (1729), p. 16. The result is far out; it ought to be about 1670 at
normal atmospheric pressure.

By encreasing the repellent force of the particles, an unelastick or incompressible fluid may become elastick, or a solid (at least a great part of it) may be changed into an elastick fluid; and, *vice versâ*, by diminishing the repellent force, an elastick fluid may be reduc'd to an unelastick fluid, or to a solid.[18]

Heat or 'fermentation' may increase this repellent force. Here we have a somewhat more comprehensible theory than the mere 'combination of fire and water' that, as we shall find, became fashionable later in the century. Desaguliers's theory was derived from a passage in Newton's *Principia* in which he derived Boyle's law on mechanical principles,[19] a passage that inspired John Dalton, as we shall find in Chapter Seven.

The prevailing confusion in the subject is well illustrated in the large and influential textbook of physics written in Dutch in 1736 by Petrus Van Musschenbroek[20] and translated into French three years later.[21] Musschenbroek begins with the usual distinction between *vapours* – aqueous and humid particles – and *exhalations*, which were all other particles, solid or liquid, but not aqueous or humid. He then discusses the various possible ways in which vapours rise into the air. First, because of heat. When 'fire insinuates itself into the little pores' of a particle of water, this expands enormously, and rises until it is in equilibrium with the air. Therefore when the barometer is low the vapours rise less.

So far so good; but Musschenbroek is worried by the fact that if a large body is stretched it breaks after a small elongation; so he supposes that the small particles themselves can expand without breaking. Another difficulty is that liquid water increases only 1/26 in volume when heated from freezing point to boiling point,[22] but a drop of water converted to vapour increases in volume 14,000 times, according to his measurements.[23] This discrepancy, he admits,

---

[18] *Ibid.*, p. 15.

[19] Isaac Newton, *Philosophiae naturalis principia mathematica*, lib. II, prop. 23.

[20] *Beginselen der matuurkunde* [etc.], Leyden, 1736.

[21] *Essai de physique par Mr Pierre Van Musschenbroek . . . traduit du Hollandois par Mr Pierre Massuet.* Leyden, 1739. (2 vol., paged as one).

[22] The modern value is approximately 1/23.

[23] The same erroneous result as Desaguliers' (Note 17).

is embarrassing. He would probably have found an explanation, *more suo*, if the concept of latent heat had been known to him.

So far he has been discussing the vapour from boiling water, but now he comes to the product of evaporation at lower temperatures, making the astonishing assumption that the specific volume of vapour relative to water is linear in Fahrenheit degrees![24] Thus even at the freezing point, water vapour would be lighter than air, and 'consequently vapour will be able to come out of water and ice in winter, and then rise in the air, as we see it actually does'.[25] From all this Musschenbroek concludes that 'fire' is the principal cause of the rise of vapours, and also of exhalations.

Among other causes are 'fermentation, corruption, mixture, and effervescence'. In this group he seems to include the production of the clouds of *vapeurs* at the base of high waterfalls, among which Niagara is mentioned. Here again we have the unresolved confusion between visible steam or cloud and invisible vapour. Again – and this suggestion, stemming from Halley perhaps, was to have a long and active history – 'Air and water have a mutual attraction, and dissolve in one-another to some extent.'[26] He instances the evaporation from a jug of hot water, the *vapeurs* (steam) from which disperse quickly in the air, apparently by this processes of solution. Finally winds take up a large quantity of vapour from water and of particles from other substances. That is why wet clothes dry more quickly in a wind.

Musschenbroek then discusses the way in which vapours and exhalations continue to rise. As the density of the air decreases with height, they can rise to various heights according to their specific gravities. But:

> The particles which are charged with fire continually lose part of it in rising through the cold air, and so become colder. Therefore they will not be able to rise farther in the atmosphere, as soon as they have become as cold as the air that surrounds them . . . There also exist other particles which, having become 14,000 times lighter than water

[24] Though D. G. Fahrenheit (1686–1736) was born at Danzig, he lived and worked so long in the Netherlands that the Dutch seem to have thought of him as one of themselves. This may help to explain Musschenbroek's amiable error.

[25] *Essai de physique*, p. 739.   [26] *Ibid.*, p. 740

after having been converted into vapour, are at least 14 times rarer and lighter than the air that surrounds our globe. These particles, which must go through the air until they reach the place at which they are in equilibrium with it, will be able to rise only to a height of 16 English miles.[27]

Thus it is clear that the vapour from boiling water has a special position as far as Musschenbroek is concerned, not being 'charged with fire' in the sense that it loses some as it ascends.

We shall meet Musschenbroek and his textbook again several times in the following chapters. It was very widely quoted, but in the eighteenth century textbooks were considered rather as reports of current scientific opinion than as divine Revelation.

In 1743 the Academy of Bordeaux 'crowned' an essay by G. E. Hamberger.[28] This suggested a new point of view, namely that only the movement of the air can cause the vapour to rise. This process is assisted by the circumstance that the vapour is warmer than the air and heats it a little, causing an upward motion. Hamberger had an elementary idea of convection. For instance after noting that vapours only slightly warm (such as lake fogs on summer nights) do not rise far, he goes on:

> However, the heat necessary to the elevation of vapour can be re-established . . . if a region filled with vapour is illuminated by the sun, for . . . the air filled with vapour will be more strongly heated by the sun's rays than will the surrounding clear air, since the former is a denser body than the latter, and bodies are more susceptible to being heated, the denser they are.[29]

The last phrase was certainly intuitive at that date.

3. WATER DISSOLVED

At about this time a book appeared at Strasbourg which, if it had attracted any attention, ought surely to have suggested the

[27] *Ibid.*, p. 741.
[28] G. E. Hamberger, *Dissertation sur la cause de l'élévation des vapeurs.* Bordeaux, 1743.
[29] *Ibid.*, p. 85.

28

answer to this puzzle. This was Daniel Bernouilli's *Hydrodynamica*,[30] in Section X of which he founded the kinetic theory of gases, demonstrating that the relations between the pressure, temperature, and volume of elastic fluids could be explained by assuming such substances to be composed of numerous particles in rapid motion. This idea was simply too revolutionary for its time, and was considered as an ingenious exercise in mathematics; it seems to have been forgotten until well into the next century.[31] We shall have occasion to return to it in Chapter Four; but now we shall consider the development of the 'solution' theory of evaporation. This is generally supposed to date from 1751,[32] but we have already noted Halley's remark, and in 1742 there was a short report by the Secretary of the *Académie Royale des Sciences* in Paris (at this time J. J. D'Ortous de Mairan) on some thoughts by Jean Bouillet about this problem.[33] Bouillet was a Correspondent of the Academy from Beziers. De Mairan says that:

> They will have all the parts of the liquid . . . in continuous movement, and this movement is to be circular or approximately so. In this way the invisible particles which happen to be at the surface will be obliged to rise up and fly off on a tangent . . .[34]

This seems to be more Cartesian than Descartes. But why, he asks, do they not at once fall back? 'For everyone knows that the particles of water and of all other liquids, however small, weigh, volume for volume, much more than those of air',[35] and by the laws of hydrostatics the heavier should come down. To get over this difficulty, Bouillet supposes that the water which evaporates is 'united' with the air, just as air absorbed by water is united with the water and forms part of it. This is clearly a solution theory, though the word is not used.

[30] Daniel Bernouilli, *Hydrodynamica, sive de viribus & motibus fluidorum commentarii*. Strasbourg, 1738.

[31] The first six paragraphs of Section X of the *Hydrodynamica* have been translated in *The world of mathematics*, James R. Newman, ed., New York, Simon and Schuster, 1956, Vol. II, pp. 774-7.

[32] Charles Le Roy, *Mém. Acad. Roy. Sci. Paris* (1751), 481-518.

[33] 'Sur l'évaporation des liquides.' *Hist. Acad. Roy. Sci. Paris* (1742), 18-21.

[34] *Ibid.*, p. 18.

[35] *Ibid.*, p. 19. Reflect, if you will, on how strange this idea sounds today.

In his 'Mémoire sur l'élévation et la suspension de l'eau dans l'air, et sur la rosée',[36] Charles Le Roy of Montpellier did use the word 'solution', and used it very well. This paper, in spite of the supersession of its physical ideas, is a most elegant piece of scientific writing, and also a landmark in the history of hygrometry.

Le Roy begins by citing Musschenbroek, Bouillet, and Barbaret. The last reference is to a paper read to the Academy of Dijon on 20 August 1752,[37] in which its author draws a very pretty picture of the process of evaporation. Particles of water are knocked out of the liquid by the great speed of the particles of fire (effect of temperature) or of air (effect of wind). But how are they sustained? By 'solution' in the air, he says, and asks us to think of spherical particles of water held up in the branches of the *parties rameuses* of the air. In fact he even imagines the air-particles prying particles of water out of the surface, 'like so many levers'![38]

The authors whom he has cited, says Le Roy, think that the mechanism by which solids dissolve in liquids is better known than that by which water is raised into the air, and that the idea of solution can 'explain or at least illuminate the mechanism of the elevation and suspension of water in air'.[39] He takes the same view, and proceeds to enlarge on it.

In the first place, true solutions are characteristically transparent; a body that might be a solution but is turbid is in a state of 'simple mechanical division'. Air containing water vapour, as distinct from fog or cloud, is just as transparent as dry air. Secondly, just as the amount of salt that water can hold in solution depends on the temperature, so does the amount of water that the air can sustain.

As evidence for the solution theory he adduces the experiment in which ice is placed in a dry glass, which soon becomes covered

[36] *Mém. Acad. Roy. Sci. Paris* (1751), 481–518.
[37] [Denis?] Barbaret, *Mém. Acad. Dijon* 1 (1769), 1–32. The apparent impossibility in the dates arises from the slowness of publication of the Paris *Mémoires*; the volume for 1751 was not published till 1754; Le Roy's paper was sent from the Academy at Montpellier, and put near the end of the volume. It may really date from 1753.
[38] *Ibid.*, p. 11.
[39] *Mém. Acad. Roy. Sci. Paris* (1751), 482.

with very small drops of water. These can come from nowhere except from the perfectly transparent air round the glass.[40]

To demonstrate the effect of temperature he simply sealed up a bottle of damp air and put it in a space where the temperature was falling. At some particular temperature the inside of the bottle became covered with dew, which disappeared when the temperature rose again. As long as the bottle remained sealed, dew would always appear at the same temperature, the lowest temperature at which the air in the bottle could hold in solution, as he thought, all the water that happened to be in the bottle when it was sealed up.

This temperature, which we should now call the dew point, Le Roy called 'le degré de saturation de l'air'.[41] He could measure it for the air in the room or outdoors by having a series of goblets, some cold water, and a thermometer. If dew formed when the water is poured into a dry goblet, he let it warm up half a degree, and poured it into another; and so on until dew just did not form. This was his hygrometer, unhandy but sound in principle, and with it he made numerous observations, finding, for example, that at Montpellier the dew-point is different for different wind directions, the south wind from the sea being the moistest, the north wind the driest. The *mistrao* (NW) and *grec* (NE) are not as dry. With the *grec* it must be moister aloft, he thought, there being usually an overcast with this wind. He also reasoned that at great heights the air, being very cold, could never hold much moisture in 'solution'.

Obviously this sort of experimentation opened new vistas in meteorology, and Le Roy was aware of it.

> The theory that we have just developed gives us precise ideas about the elevation and suspension of water in the air, and about the causes of precipitation; ideas which, it seems to me, must be substituted for the vague notions of the rarefaction and condensation of vapour, with which we have been contented up till now.[42]

It was a great clarifier of ideas. Le Roy pointed out that the ideas 'dry air' and 'moist air' do not, as ordinarily believed, refer to its

[40] An experiment performed very elegantly by the *Accademia del Cimento* in Florence about 1660.

[41] *Mém. Acad. Roy. Sci. Paris* (1751), 490.   [42] *Ibid.*, p. 494.

absolute water-content but to the amount of water it contains relative to what it could contain at the prevailing temperature. Dry air on a summer day, he noted, can contain more water than very moist air in winter.

But there were ideas that it did not clarify, at least for Le Roy. The weight of the air, he thought, is partly to be attributed to the dissolved water. The air is a fluid composed of two components 'of which the specific gravities are prodigiously different'.[43] As far as we know, he did not even entertain the thought that water vapour could be specifically lighter than air. Nevertheless his paper was certainly one of the most important contributions to meteorological literature in the eighteenth century.

The solution theory found several champions, one of the most convincing being the Reverend Hugh Hamilton, a Professor of Natural Philosophy at Dublin, who set himself to multiply proofs of it.[44] For example, he quoted an experiment due to Hermann Boerhaave in which a bubble of air over air-free water is gradually absorbed, arguing that this proves that air dissolves in water, so why not water in air? He also pointed out further similarities between evaporation and the solution of solids in liquids; for instance:

(1) Just as the solution of salt in water is greatly hastened by stirring, so evaporation is accelerated by the motion of the air;

(2) Heat promotes, cold inhibits, both solution and evaporation;

(3) Just as dew or hoar-frost results when moist air is cooled, so salt is deposited from a strong solution on cooling it;

(4) Both the solution of salt, etc., and the evaporation of liquids, produce cold.[45]

When Hamilton's paper was read, someone remembered that nine years before, Benjamin Franklin had sent in a paper on the same

[43] Ibid., p. 496.   [44] Hugh Hamilton, Phil. Trans. 55 (1765), 146–81.

[45] According to G. Gazzeri in the 1841 edition of the Saggi di naturali esperienze fatte nell' Accademia del Cimento, p. XXVI, the fact that water boiling in a vacuum becomes colder is noted in an unpublished Diary of the Academy for 8 August 1662. The cold produced by evaporation was rediscovered by G. W. Richmann (Nov. Comm. Petrop. 1 (1750), 284–90 and correctly attributed to the evaporation by William Cullen five years later (Edinb. Phil. Soc., Essays Phys. & Lit. 2 (1755), 159–71).

subject, supporting the solution theory. This was then published with apologies.[46]

The solution theory of evaporation was wide open to a serious objection. It could not account for the evaporation of liquids in a vacuum. That liquids evaporated in a vacuum was well known to the earliest experimenters with air pumps, Guericke and Boyle, though careful *ad hoc* investigation had to wait for Nils Wallerius, who in 1738 published a paper entitled 'De ascensu vaporum in vacuo'.[47] After careful experiments with water, and also with wine, in a vacuum, weighing them at intervals, Wallerius not only demonstrated evaporation, but was obliged to conclude that the vapour could *ascend* in the vacuum. This disposed of the idea that vapour ascends because it is specifically lighter than air; it could not possibly be lighter than a vacuum.

Wallerius was not opposing the solution theory, for it had not been stated at that time. He is frankly puzzled, and notes that vapours can scarcely be molecules made of water and fire, even if fire weighs less than nothing; for how, then, would ice evaporate, even on mountain-tops, as it does? Nor could vapour be bubbles with rarefied air inside, or even with nothing inside, for these would not rise in a vacuum; and at any rate he cannot believe in such bubbles for common-sense reasons, for example they would collapse.

Wallerius's paper, in a Swedish journal, seems to have remained almost unknown. In 1771, Henry Home, Lord Kames, a Scottish Jurist, amusing himself with natural philosophy in his old age, published a spirited defence of the solution theory,[48] in which he maintained that 'no fair reasoner can refuse his assent to this theory, when he thus finds it making a capital branch of the general theory of dissolution, espoused by all chymists'.[49] But evaporation from boiling water is different; it is due to the mutual repulsion between the particles of water when heated very hot.

Kames knew that the solution theory will not account for evaporation *in vacuo*. But:

[46] Benjamin Franklin, *Phil. Trans.* 55 (1765), 182–92.
[47] Nils Wallerius, *Acta Litteraria, Upsala* 4 (1738), 339–46.
[48] *Edinb. Phil. Soc., Essays & Obs.* 3 (1771), 80–99.   [49] *Ibid.*, p. 90.

The best way to account for this supposed evaporation, at least the easiest, is to deny the fact, which may be done *bona fide*, for I have not heard of any experiment that verifies it.[50]

There is no reason to doubt Lord Kames's *bona fides*, but it is hard to account for the result obtained in 1777 by a Dr Dobson of Liverpool, who 'weighed two china saucers, each containing three ounces of water'. One was placed out of doors, the other

> under the receiver of an air pump. The air was exhausted, and the pistons occasionally worked, to draw off any of the water which might be supposed to be converted into vapour. After four hours the saucers were again accurately weighed; that in the open air had lost one drachm and eight grains; the weight of the other was not sensibly diminished.[51]

It is difficult to believe that the Doctor was both honest and competent.

In 1780 Lorenzo Pignotti of Pisa examined the solution theory and approved of it.[52] He disposed of the objection that water evaporates in a vacuum by two suggestions: first, an immense amount of air comes out of the water, and water dissolves in this; second, if evaporation really does take place in a true vacuum, it must be an entirely different process.

The argument was carried a stage further by the celebrated Swiss geologist and physicist Horace Benedict de Saussure in his *Essais sur l'hygrométrie*, one of the monuments of eighteenth-century physics.[53] We may summarize his theory as follows: evaporation is the effect of an intimate union of fire with water, producing an elastic fluid, lighter than air, which he calls *vapour*. (He had shown that the fluid produced by evaporating water in a vacuum exerted a pressure that could be measured with a barometer, and that this pressure depended on the temperature.) When such vapour is formed *in vacuo* or from boiling water, he calls it *pure elastic vapour*; but at ordinary temperatures and in air the vapour penetrates the air,

[50] *Ibid.*, p. 99.   [51] *Phil. Trans.* 67 (1777), 256.
[52] L. Pignotti, *Congetture meteorologiche*. Florence, 1780, pp. 75–103.
[53] H. B. de Saussure, *Essais sur l'hygrométrie*, Neuchâtel, 1783. His theory of evaporation is summarized on pp. 257–8.

34

mixes with it, suffers a true solution and takes the name *dissolved elastic vapour*.

It will be seen that this differs importantly from the original solution theory, in that it demands the union of 'fire' with the water *before* the latter can be dissolved in the air. One may ask why the idea of solution was needed at all, and indeed this is just what was asked, as we shall see. Meanwhile let us review, as Louis Cotte did in 1774,[54] the various theories of evaporation in vogue at this period: (1) The theory that water was divided into molecules fine enough for the air to carry them up and sustain them. This is really Descartes's theory, and was out of fashion at the time. (2) The theory that fire united with water, increasing the volume of water particles until they were light enough to float. This was modified soon after by supposing that the fire combined with the particles of water to produce an elastic fluid. (3) The solution theory.

Cotte omitted, perhaps on purpose, the electrical theory of evaporation. Between about 1730 and 1760 there was an immense amount of experimentation on static electricity, and all sorts of people quite naturally thought of bringing in this new 'force' to account for puzzling phenomena. In 1742 Desaguliers tried to explain evaporation in this manner:[55]

> The air which flows at top of the surface of the waters is electrical, and so much the more as the weather is hotter. Now in the same manner as small particles of water jump towards the electric tube, may not those particles jump towards the particles of air, which have much more specific gravity than very small particles of water, and adhere to them? then the air in motion having carried off the particles of water, and driving them away as soon as it has made them electrical, they repel one another, and also the particles of air. This is the reason why a cubic inch of vapour is lighter than a cubic inch of air, which would not happen, if the particles of vapour were only carried off in the interstices of air, because then a cubic inch of air, loaded with vapour, would be made specifically heavier than an inch of dry air; which is contrary to experiments, which shew us by the barometer, that air which is moist, or full of vapours, is always lighter than dry air.

[54] L. Cotte, *Traité de météorologie*. Paris, 1774, p. 39.
[55] J. T. Desaguliers, *Phil. Trans.* 42 (1742), 140–3.

I do not propose to pay much attention in this book to the eighteenth-century electrical speculations about rain, which were entirely sterile. The above passage is notable, however, because it is the first attempt known to me to get away from the idea that vapour must be an *additional* weight in the air, though the celebrated philosopher Christian Wolff thought that water vapour remains in the air because it has *the same* specific gravity, and also pointed out that the transparency (or otherwise) of the air depends 'not on the amount of vapour, but on the way in which it is arranged in the air. Clear air can thus have as much vapour in it as turbid air'.[56]

4. WATER AND FIRE

We must now return to the hypothesis that water vapour is a mixture, or compound, of water and 'fire', the latter almost universally considered in the eighteenth-century to be an extremely tenuous and almost if not quite imponderable *substance*, which came to be called 'caloric'. The staunchest defender of this theory of evaporation was Jean André Deluc, who played such a notable part in the development of our subject that a few biographical details may be desirable. Born at Geneva, he was engaged in commerce and politics until he moved to England in 1773; but as a young man he made a hobby of geology and meteorology and made many scientific journeys in the Alps near Geneva. He himself dated his interest in barometry and barometric hypsometry from the year 1749, when he was only 22.[57] This developed into a burning desire to solve the problem of the variations of the barometer and to produce a satisfactory theory of rain.

Shortly after he moved to England he was made a Fellow of the Royal Society and given the not very onerous post of reader to

[56] Chr. Wolff, *Allerhand nützliche Versuche, dadurch zu genauer Erkänntniss der Natur und Kunst der Weg gebahnet wird* [etc.] 2nd ed., Halle, 1745–7, Vol. 2, p. 221. (*Ed. princ.* 1722).

[57] Deluc, *Recherches sur les modifications de l'atmosphère* (2 vols., 4°, Geneva, 1772. 2nd. ed., 4 vols., 8°, Paris, 1784), ¶ 111. References to this work will be given to paragraph (¶) numbers, which are the same in the two editions, and continuous throughout. It will be referred to as *Modifications*.

Queen Charlotte, which he held until his death. He was able to continue his scientific studies with more freedom than before, and produced a number of works, of which the most interesting to us is the *Idées sur la météorologie* which appeared in 1786 and 1787,[58] and will be referred to extensively in later chapters. His contemporary reputation was far in excess of his real ability. He was a close friend of Watt and Priestley, and was strongly influenced by their researches, especially Priestley's. Certainly one of the most interesting characters in our story, he was also one of the least attractive; a formidable controversialist, he had remarkable powers of self-deception, or rather a complete inability to criticise his own ideas. Nevertheless these ideas were sometimes fruitful, and in the history of meteorological instruments he has an honoured place.[59]

Deluc's *Modifications* was first published in 1772, but there is evidence that it was substantially complete ten years earlier. Thus we may suppose that by 1760 he had come to the conclusion that water vapour is lighter than air, and that it is composed of water and fire, to the proof of which proposition he devotes many pages (¶ 675–708). Interestingly enough it does not, at this date, matter to his hypothesis whether fire is 'a real substance, or a simple modification' (note to ¶ 675); though at a later period in his life he had no doubt of its material existence.

Part of the argument is that fire has a greater affinity for water than for air; does not water extinguish fire, attracting it into itself? Moreover the temperature is lower at high altitudes, where the air is dryer. By condensing on a body that is cold enough, the vapours themselves show that they contain fire (¶ 691), and liquids are cooled by evaporation (¶ 693). (The reader may notice that these last two phenomena had been used as arguments for the solution theory.) He had noted that a cloud through which he passed on a mountain was warmer than the clear air around it, and that the formation of fog and hoar frost is often accompanied by a rise in temperature (¶ 694–6).

[58] Deluc, *Idées sur la météorologie*. London, 1786; Paris, 1787. As the pagination differs in the two printings, we shall also refer to this work by paragraph numbers (¶), taken from the Paris edition.

[59] For Deluc and the barometer, see W. E. K. Middleton, *The history of the barometer*, Baltimore, 1964, *passim*.

He devotes several pages to an attempt to demonstrate that there is enough fire, even in winter, to produce evaporation (¶ 684–90).

Support for the theory soon came from the great chemist Antoine Laurent de Lavoisier, in a memoir read to the *Académie des Sciences* in 1777, with a title that suggests an advance in thinking.[60] 'In this memoir,' begins Lavoisier,

> I shall suppose that the planet we inhabit is everywhere surrounded by a very subtle fluid that penetrates all the substances composing the world, apparently without exception; that this fluid, which I shall call *igneous fluid, the substance of fire, heat, and light*,[61] tends to come to an equilibrium in all substances, but does not penetrate them all with equal ease; and finally, that this fluid sometimes exists in a free state, sometimes in a fixed state, combined with other substances.

This opinion, he says, is commonly received. The passage is a succinct statement of the material theory of heat.

Now the igneous fluid in a body is partly free, partly combined. The temperature[62] is a measure of the free part of the igneous fluid; so that in any reaction we may judge whether heat (*matière du feu*) is emitted or absorbed by seeing whether the reagents become hotter or colder. Therefore, as evaporation is accompanied by cold, there must be an absorption of heat; it has combined with the liquid in order to form vapour.

Lavoisier then describes an experiment in which a small vessel of sulphuric ether is closed by means of a bladder (wired on tight), and put under the receiver of an air pump, together with a barometer. When as good a vacuum as possible has been produced, the bladder is punctured by an ingenious mechanism. The ether then 'evaporates with an astonishing rapidity, and is transformed into an elastic fluid, which sustains the barometer at about 8 or 10 inches in winter, and at 20 to 25 inches during the hottest summer weather. While the

[60] A. L. Lavoisier, 'De la combinaison de la matiére du feu avec les fluides évaporables, et de la formation des fluides élastiques aëriformes.' *Mém Acad. Roy. Sci. Paris* (1777), 420–32.

[61] *Fluide igné, matière du feu, de la chaleur, & de la lumière.* The italics are in the original.

[62] *Intensité de la chaleur.* Lavoisier later uses the word *température.*

ether is evaporating it becomes much colder.'[63] If now the air is let in, the barometer goes back to its ordinary height, but this does not condense the ether, which remains in the state of an elastic fluid. Other volatile liquids, even water, produce the same effects to a less marked degree.

With admirable clarity Lavoisier interprets the experiment, which proves:

> . . . three things: the first, that the weight of the atmosphere is a resistance to be overcome, a force opposed to the vaporization of fluids; the second, that as soon as this compressive force no longer exists, evaporable fluids start to expand, and change into aeriform elastic fluids, varieties of air; finally the third, that this change of ordinary fluids into elastic fluids is accompanied by an absorption of heat which takes place at the expense of all the surrounding bodies.[64]

Only hindsight makes one wonder what Lavoisier would have answered if he had been asked what would happen if some volatile liquid were poured out in the empty space between the earth and the moon. Where would the heat have come from to evaporate it, or would it not evaporate? Finally 'every vapour, every gas, and in general every aeriform elastic fluid, is a combination of heat (*matière du feu*) with a fluid, or even with some volatile solid body.'[65] Regarding this last conclusion De Saussure pointed out[66] that in ordinary gases the heat must be much more firmly bound to the substance than in vapours, which can be liquefied by simple cooling.

Lavoisier's main conclusions about vapour were adopted by Deluc, though possibly he came to them independently. But Deluc was readier than Lavoisier to form mechanical – or indeed any other – hypotheses. Expansible fluids, as he called them by 1786, were composed of discrete, moving particles. These do not necessarily move in straight lines, but different substances have particles with various kinds of motion – a hypothesis without issue and apparently made just for the fun of it. But, more seriously, aqueous vapours have the mechanical properties of gases, 'and exercise them in

[63] *Mém. Acad. Roy. Sci. Paris* (1777), 425.   [64] *Ibid.*, pp. 425–6.
[65] *Ibid.*, p. 432.   [66] *Essais sur l'hygrométrie*, p. 186.

complete independence of these fluids'.[67] The vapour-pressure,[68] he says, is independent of the presence of air; at the same temperature it is the same in the air as in a vacuum, but the presence of the air enables a small amount of water to remain in the form of vapour under the pressure of the atmosphere.[69] These statements have led to Deluc being called the precursor of Dalton, but this is true only in a very limited sense.[70]

It is interesting that De Saussure, whose hair hygrometer Deluc had compared very unfavourably with a much inferior hygrometer of his own,[71] flatly accused Deluc of appropriating his ideas about water vapour.[72] De Saussure had every reason to be annoyed with Deluc, but in reality De Saussure might with equal justice have been accused of appropriating ideas from Lavoisier. These things were 'in the air'.

But Deluc, in his ungovernable urge to 'explain' everything, did not stop here. For instance he has a quasi-statistical theory of the reason the maximum vapour-pressure varies rapidly with temperature. If there is too much vapour for the temperature, the particles of water get so near together that they join with each other more readily with the particles of fire.[73] And with characteristic brashness he claimed to have suspected that the air is not a simple substance before Priestley discovered its complex nature.[74] It is worth noting that in 1782 and 1783 Deluc became very friendly with the members of the 'Lunar Society', especially with Watt and Priestley.[75]

In the later chapters of the *Idées sur la météorologie*, he let his ingenuity run riot; and yet he was not merely a crank. His philosophy is summed up in the following passage:

[67] J. A. Deluc, *Idées*, ¶ 5.   [68] In our terms, to avoid circumlocution.

[69] *Idées*, ¶ 14.   [70] See also Chapter 7.

[71] For a study of this controversy see W. E. K. Middleton, *Q. J. Roy. Meteorol. Soc.* 68 (1942), 247–61.

[72] H. B. de Saussure, *Défense de l'hygromètre à cheveu, pour servir de suite aux essais sur l'hygrométrie*, Geneva 1788, p. 31.

[73] Deluc, *Idées*, ¶ 8–10.

[74] *Ibid.*, ¶ 102. According to Robert E. Schofield (*The Lunar Society of Birmingham*, Oxford, Clarendon Press, 1963, p. 240), James Watt described Deluc as 'a modest ingeneous man'. The ingenuity is certain, but the modesty is hard to find in his works, and perhaps he was a bit of a politician.

[75] See Schofield, *passim*.

What is essential in nature, as soon as we concern ourselves with physics, is that phenomena have causes; and our one and only means of assigning reasonable causes to phenomena, where we do not discover them at once, is by analogy.[76]

He seems to have remained unaware of the dangers of arguing from analogy, and to have believed firmly that any 'explanation' is better than the admission of total ignorance. This led him to postulate the existence of unknown and undemonstrable 'aeriform fluids', the properties of which it would be tedious to recount.

But on occasion he could come down to earth, and in a paper published in 1792 he gives an eminently reasonable account of the process of evaporation as it was known at that time, water vapour (which he calls 'steam' for brevity) being considered as 'an expansible fluid, composed of water and fire'.[77] In one respect he improves on Lavoisier when he says (p. 401) that the portion of the liquid that disappears in evaporation 'is carried away by a quantity of fire proceeding from the liquid itself'. He gives an 'abstract' of his theory in eleven 'laws of hygrology' that it would be interesting to reproduce if they were shorter.[78] Fortunately he provides a concise summary in the following words (p. 424):

> . . . it may safely be concluded: That the product of evaporation is always of the same nature, namely, an expansible fluid, which, either alone or mixed with air, affects the manometer by pressure and the hygrometer by moisture, without any difference arising from the presence or absence of air; at least without any perceived hitherto.

This conclusion obtained the powerful support of Alessandro Volta, who in a letter to the editor of the *Neue Journal der Physik* in 1796 agreed with Deluc 'that the quantity of vapour and its pressure, at a given temperature, is entirely independent of the presence or absence of air'.[79] Even before this the subject had been greatly advanced by the more precise experiments of Marc Auguste Pictet, Professor of Philosophy at Geneva, whose *Essais de physique*

[76] *Idées*, ¶ 531. We shall return to the *Idées* in Chapter 6.
[77] J. A. Deluc, 'On Evaporation'. *Phil. Trans.* 82 (1792), 400–24.
[78] They occupy about five quarto pages, 401–6.
[79] A. Volta, *Gren's neue J. der Phys.* 3 (1796), 479.

had been published there in 1790. Pictet had believed in the solution theory, because of the very specious arguments of De Saussure, but his experiments had led him to regard 'fire' as the only agent producing evaporation.[80] People were beginning to measure the properties of water vapour at various temperatures in the 1790's.[81] And at the end of the century M. Van Marum, by carefully controlled experiments,[82] was able to show that the widely accepted belief[83] that electricity increases evaporation is quite unfounded.

[80] Pictet, *Essais*, p. 155.

[81] *e.g.* G. G. Schmidt, *Gren's neue J. der Phys.* 4 (1797), 251–319, who managed to find the vapour-pressure zero at the freezing point.

[82] M. Van Marum, *Ann. der Phys.* 1 (1799), 112–22.

[83] This was due to the Abbé Nollet, *Recherches sur les causes particulières des phenomenes électriques.* Paris, 1764, p. 324.

Chapter Three

THE STRUCTURE OF CLOUDS AND THEIR SUSPENSION

I wandered lonely as a cloud
That floats on high o'er vales and hills.
                                        —Wordsworth.

1. THE TINY PARTICLES

However difficult it may have been to understand the processes by which the invisible vapour of water is raised and diffused through the atmosphere – and we have just seen what a serious problem this was – the suspension of visible and obviously material clouds, often of immense size, was bound to present even greater difficulties to the slowly developing science of meteorology. For clouds were known to be made of water in some form or other, and water is several hundred times as heavy as air. How then can a cloud float? We now know that it cannot; every cloud-particle is slowly sinking through the air it is in, but this may indeed be rising; or the cloud may continually be dissolving at its lower boundary as the particles subside. But this sophisticated resolution of the paradox belongs to the last hundred years, and we must follow the steps that led to it.

Aristotle was, for once, on the right track. 'Drops of water,' he wrote, 'ride aloft because of their minuteness and rest on the air, like minute particles of earth or gold that often float on water.'[1]

For Descartes, too, there was a similar but better-developed explanation:

As [the particles of the cloud] have a large surface in relation to the quantity of matter in them, the resistance of the air that they would

---

[1] Aristotle, *Meteorologica*, I, 12, trans. H. D. P. Lee. London, Heinemann, 1952 (Loeb Classical Library).

43

have to divide if they were to descend can easily have more force to hinder them than their weight has to drive them down.[2]

The reader familiar with the history of mechanics will recognize this suggestion as purely Aristotelian, and may reflect that Descartes could have learned better from Galileo if he had waited for one more year. But he improves on this, suggesting that the winds blow 'more upwards than downwards', and may not only sustain the clouds but cause them to rise. Furthermore vapours coming out of the earth, or heat, can expand the air below them; the cold above, contracting the upper air, can draw them upwards. But he warns us that the droplets, or particles of ice – he realized that clouds could be made of these – can only be very small, because otherwise they would promptly fall to earth; in fact they would be rain or snow.

There is no doubt whatever that Descartes was nearer to an explanation of the suspension of clouds than anyone else for at least another century. But I should warn the reader that the above ex- cerpts taken alone do him more than justice. It is evident throughout *Les météores* that the rigorous ideas of continuity expressed in his theory of vortices do not get carried over into his meteorology; and he treats a cloud as an entity – a sort of balloon – that can be pushed about by a wind, or compressed between several winds. The latter idea had important repercussions that will appear in our next two chapters.

Twenty years after *Les météores* Otto von Guericke, the mayor of Magdeburg, had invented the air pump and was doing those celebrated pneumatic experiments reported fully only in 1672.[3] It is evident that Guericke also considered a cloud as an object having a definite specific gravity.

The air, according to our idea, can be divided into steps or regions. Each kind of cloud, heavier or lighter, keeps to its own particular one of these regions, in which its weight matches that of the air. But if the air were everywhere compressed it would be equally heavy above and

[2] Descartes, *Les météores* (1637). In *Oeuvres*, publ. par Ch. Adam & Paul Tannery, vol. 6, Paris, 1902, p. 291.

[3] *Ottonis de Guericke Experimenta nova (ut vocantur) Magdeburgica de vacuo spatio* [etc.] Amsterdam, 1672.

44

below, so that the clouds could not be formed in different ways in different regions; but as in water, where things either sink to the bottom or float, so the clouds would either descend to the earth, or go up to the highest part of the air.[4]

2. LITTLE BUBBLES

But Guericke produced clouds of his own in the laboratory. He took two flasks with taps, evacuated one, joined them together and opened the taps. The equalization of pressure caused the air in the unevacuated flask to 'give up its surplus moisture', which then became visible.

> This can easily be observed in the form of very small drops (*in guttulis minimis*), which gradually sink to the bottom of the flask. The process is more noticeable, the better the inside of the flask is provided with moisture; for then the little bubbles (*bullulae*) are produced more copiously, so that they . . . form a fog. On the introduction of a little air this can collect into clouds.[5]

I have quoted this passage because of the mysterious juxtaposition of *guttulae* and *bullulae*. Is this an instance of what H. W. Fowler in *A dictionary of modern English usage* called 'elegant variation', or did Guericke think he had found two different phenomena? I believe the second explanation is the more likely, for the following reasons: first, the two Latin words have quite distinct meanings; second, the appearance of such a flask can differ markedly, depending (to anticipate Chapter Eight) on the concentration of condensation-nuclei as well as on the amount of moisture available.[6] With only a few nuclei, comparatively large droplets are formed, which sink fairly quickly to the bottom of the flask; when large numbers are available, they share the moisture and the drops are smaller, remaining in suspension for much longer. It seems probable to me that Guericke, whose parsimony with words was quite uncharacteristic of his age, really meant to indicate that he thought the little particles were hollow.

The next reference to little bubbles that I have seen is in the paper read by Halley in 1688 and published in 1693, already referred to in

---

[4] *Ibid.*, p. 72.   [5] *Ibid.*, pp. 88–89.   [6] See p. 172 below.

Chapter II.[7] Halley is generally given credit for originating the theory that clouds float because they are made of little bubbles. Actually he did not believe this at all; as I have already shown, he believed that invisible water vapour was enabled to rise because atoms of water had been expanded into 'shells or bubbles'.[8] Twice on page 473 of his paper he says clearly that clouds are formed of 'drops'; in one instance, 'visible drops'.[9] The earliest clear statement of the vesicular nature of *clouds* that I have found dates from 1701 and is the work of a Jesuit, Pardies,[10] who was trying to refute an idea which he says was commonly held, that the 'vapours' composing a cloud are attached together 'as if by glue', forming 'a single body which must easily be sustained in the air because of the immense extent of its surface'.[11] Pardies doubts, not whether such a supposed body would remain aloft, but whether the particles of clouds are any more strongly held together than those of water; and after all, air may easily pass upwards through water and escape.

Therefore he supposes the clouds to be made of little bubbles. These cannot be filled with ordinary air, but must hold 'fiery spirits' or 'a very subtle and very rarefied air'. Because the walls of the bubbles have various thicknesses, they do not all float at the same height, and thus fogs and clouds are explained.[12] Pardies presents all this as if it were his own original concept.

Halley's idea is correctly referred to in a dissertation by Johannes Cruegerus, published in 1701 at Jena.[13] The possibility that cloud-particles are vesicular is also mentioned, but without very much enthusiasm.

In the first volume of the transactions of the new Berlin Academy,

---

[7] *Phil. Trans.* 17 (1693), 468–73. Ritter, in *Ann. Soc. Météorol. de France* 33 (1885), 262, says that the 'vesicular' hypothesis was first given by Leibnitz in 1668. I have been unable to identify this reference.

[8] See p. 23 above.

[9] This paper is again referred to in Chapter 5 (p. 95).

[10] *Mém. de Trevoux*, Mar.–April 1701, pp. 155–66. This Pardies was not the one who argued about light with Newton.

[11] *Ibid.*, p. 157.

[12] The physical identity of fogs and clouds seems never to have been seriously denied; therefore fogs need no special treatment in this chapter.

[13] *Dissertatio academica de barometris.*

founded by the Elector Frederick III at the instigation of the great philosopher Gottfried Wilhelm Leibnitz, the latter had something to say about the problem[14] by way of editorial comment on a short paper by one Chauvin.[15] Leibnitz tries to meet the objection that if the air included in the bubble were rarer than the air around it, the bubble would be compressed until it was equally dense. He brings in the effect of heat 'or something analogous to heat in fermentation and similar natural processes'. But why should the air within the bubble remain warmer? Because the air outside is moving faster than the bubble [!]. so that new air will strike it and impart its heat to it, 'just as we feel the hand, in warm or cold water, get warmer or cooler if we move it about, than if we leave it still'.[16] He then makes extensive calculations about the necessary thinness of a bubble in relation to its diameter, if it is to float.

After writing the above paragraph I suddenly realized that I had paid no attention to the paper by Chauvin which occasioned Leibnitz's comment, though both were equally nugatory. So are we affected by the names of great men! The truth is that the great philosopher, mathematician, and statesman was much less fortunate in his physics; and while this particular fantasy was not very influential, we shall have to return in the next chapter to another red herring of his, the scent of which took sixty years to evaporate from the scientific trail.

In 1711 and 1712 William Derham, F.R.S., the Rector of Upminster in Essex, gave the Boyle Lectures, which were later published.[17] In this work, which went through fourteen editions by 1800, Derham wrote so enthusiastically about vesicles that he was thought by some to have originated the idea. What was original with him was the claim to have observed them

with a microscope, as they swim about in a ray of the sun let into a dark room, with warm water underneath; where some of the vapours appear large, some smaller sphaerules, according (no doubt) to the

[14] G. W. Leibnitz, *Miscellanea Berolinensia* I (1710), 123–8.
[15] Etienne Chauvin, *Ibid.*, p. 120–2.   [16] *Ibid.*, p. 124.
[17] William Derham, *Physico-Theology: or, a Demonstration of the Being and Attributes of God, from His Works of Creation* [etc.]. London, 1713.

larger or lesser quantities of heat blowing them up, and carrying them off.[18]

I am not sure whether Newton believed in vesicles; he seems to have referred to cloud particles as 'globules', a word that might apply to either bubbles or droplets.[19] But Newton had not been dead ten years when another Englishman of much less importance but great common sense, John Rowning, took a hard look at these bubbles, and asked:

> *First*, how comes the air in the bubbles to be specifically lighter than that without, since the sun's rays, which act upon the water, are equally dense over all its surface? *Secondly*, if it could be possible for rarer air to be separated from the denser ambient air ... what would hinder the external air from reducing that, which is inclosed in the bubbles, immediately to the same degree of coldness, and specific gravity with itself; (cold being readily communicated through such thin shells of water) ...?
> *Thirdly*, if we should grant all the rest of the supposition, yet the following difficulty will still remain. If clouds are made up of bubbles of water filled with air, why do not those bubbles always expand, when the ambient air is rarefied, and presses less upon them than it did before; and why are they not condensed, when the ambient air is condensed by the accumulation of the superior air? But if this condensation and rarefaction should happen to them, the clouds would always continue at the same height, contrary to observation; and we should never have any rain.[20]

Another textbook-writer, Desaguliers, also stated his disbelief in the little bubbles, but for reasons less solid; he speculated that the cause of the 'rise of vapours' might be electrical.[21]

Something new seems to have been added to the argument in 1743 by Christian Gottlieb Kratzenstein, a young man who carried off a prize offered by the Academy of Sciences at Bordeaux.[22]

[18] *Ibid.*, p. 49.

[19] See Newton, *Opticks*, 4th ed., London, 1730, Book II, part III, props. 3 and 5.

[20] John Rowning, *A compendious system of natural philosophy*, 2 vol. in 4 parts, Cambridge, 1735–42, Part II, pp. 132–3. This textbook had six editions by 1767.

[21] J. T. Desaguliers, *Phil. Trans.* 42 (1742), 140–3.

[22] C. G. Kratzenstein, *Théorie de l'élévation des vapeurs & des exhalaisons démontrée mathématiquement, qui a remporté le prix au jugement de l'Académie Royale des Belles-Lettres, Sciences & Arts*. Bordeaux, 1743.

Producing a cloud of particles by a method similar to that of Guericke, he noticed – as Guericke had also done – the fleeting iridescent
colours that can be observed at the beginning of the expansion when
the operation is performed in a beam of sunlight. We now know that
these colours are due to diffraction, and can, indeed, be used to estimate the diameter of particles; but Kratzenstein thought they were
colours like those of the soap bubbles that had been investigated by
Newton, and used them to estimate the thickness of the shells of the
putative vesicles. He also made an estimate of their diameter by
comparing them with a human hair under the microscope. The two
results taken together indicated that the vesicles would not be nearly
light enough to float; and could only 'float' by virtue of the viscosity
of the air, or rise in ascending currents. Still, he thought that the
particles were vesicular, because clouds alone did not produce rain-
bows – an objection that was to need more than a century to overcome.

I shall make a leap of 40 years in order to record De Saussure's
opinion of all this. That excellent experimenter had convinced himself that clouds were vesicular; convinced himself, moreover, beyond
the possibility of changing his mind, that they were light enough to
float and even to rise in still air. The reason was that he had *seen*
them. When he examined with a lens the surface of a hot cup of
coffee or other dark liquid, the behaviour of the little cloud particles
was such that he was convinced they were bubbles.

> The lightness of these little spheres, their whiteness, their appearance,
> absolutely different to that of solid globules, their perfect resemblance
> to the more voluminous bubbles that are seen to float on the surface
> of the liquid, all leave no doubt of their nature. It is enough to see them
> to be convinced that they are hollow spheres, similar, except in size,
> to those we make with soapy water.[23]

Furthermore, he has observed them in clouds on the mountains, by
holding a strong magnifier in one hand and a polished black surface
in the other. They look just like the ones observed over the hot liquid.
No matter if Kratzenstein should be right about the thickness of
their walls, as far as he is concerned they are hollow and they float.[24]

[23] *Essais sur l'hygrométrie*, p. 201.   [24] *Ibid.*, pp. 204–5.

De Saussure repeated the apparent optical objections to full drop-lets. It is very interesting that he was aware of the small circles, or coronae, as we now call them, around the heavenly bodies; but, so convinced was he that clouds are normally vesicular, that he ascribed these to the formation of drops in them; were they not the pre-cursors of rain?[25]

Another phenomenon very difficult to explain was the almost constant height of the cloud-base for long periods of time, as seen against the mountains. The idea of a condensation level was decades away.

De Saussure tried to repeat Kratzenstein's observations of colours. Instead of seeing a rapidly changing colour, he saw a great number of colours all at once, and concludes that 'each of these vesicles is a bubble similar to a soap bubble; it must therefore be thicker at the bottom, thinner at the top'. He does not believe that the colours can form a basis for estimating their thicknesses.[26]

But even if Kratzenstein's estimates should be correct, the vesicles can still float. Their lightness may be partly due to an adhering 'atmosphere', very light. He asserts:

> Most physicists believe that almost all bodies are surrounded by a fluid, much rarer than air, and that this fluid adheres to them and forms a sort of atmosphere round them.[27]

The fact that little bubbles will float about on a hot liquid is adduced in support of this idea. But what is this atmosphere? Fire, the electric fluid, the 'subtle air' that some physicists distinguish from common air; or some other 'aeriform fluid'?

> Mr Priestley has discovered airs of so many different kinds that it would seem permissible to physicists to suppose others of such a nature and such a density as natural phenomena seem to require.[28]

Mr Priestley had a good deal to answer for in the effervescent *milieu* of the physics of 1780; but it may be said in his favour that he identified 'airs', rather than imagining them.

Later, De Saussure rather favours the electric fluid, because of the outbreaks of rain that seem to follow lightning flashes. Could it not

[25] *Ibid.*, p. 206.   [26] *Ibid.*, p. 210.   [27] *Ibid.*, p. 210.   [28] *Ibid.*, p. 212.

be that great numbers of the vesicles are suddenly 'deprived, by a sudden explosion, of the wings that sustain them', run together into drops, and give rise to cloudbursts?[29]

A serious problem remains – a problem, incidentally, which seems to have been almost ignored hitherto – how are the vesicles formed? It may seem strange to us that this aspect of the question could have been neglected for a century; but it was. De Saussure, of course, does not know, but he speculates that it is a sort of crystallization. This, he thinks, is rendered more probable because water in that form seems able to resist freezing; indeed, he has seen clouds and fogs 'composed of these vesicles, sustain themselves in the air even when the thermometer is several degrees below freezing point'.[30] They *are* liquid, because when they condense on a solid body the resulting rime is not a mass of little spheres but a collection of delicate crystals.

I cannot leave De Saussure on this subject without attempting to translate from his elegant French a paragraph on the apparently instantaneous formation of clouds:

I have often observed a very remarkable phenomenon that seems as if it could cast some light on this question [of the formation of vesicles]. When I was caught by rainy weather on the summit or the slope of some high mountain, I used to try to glimpse the formation of the clouds that I saw being born at almost every moment on the forests or meadows below me. No fog would cover the surface of these, and the air around them would be perfectly clear and transparent; but suddenly, here and there, one of these clouds would appear without my ever being able to perceive the first instant of its formation. In a place that my eye had just left, where two seconds earlier nothing whatever existed, I would suddenly see one, already grown to at least two or three fathoms[31] in diameter. Is it not natural to think that in the air, saturated with elastic and transparent vapour, that covered the surface where these clouds were formed, there was lacking only a certain condition for this vapour to be changed into vesicles, and that

[29] *Ibid.*, p. 216.
[30] *Ibid.*, p. 213. This must be one of the earliest statements of the fact of supercooling in clouds.
[31] *Toises.* 1 *toise* = 6 Paris feet = 1.95 metres approximately.

the moment this condition existed, these vesicles would form and produce a cloud?[32]

We have all seen this phenomenon, perhaps in the mountains, perhaps in the blue sky of a summer morning. It is very striking, and in the absence of one necessary physical principle,[33] very puzzling.

J. A. Deluc became an adherent of the vesicle theory. In some hypsometric observations in October 1758 he found the calculated difference in height between two stations independent of the presence or absence of a cloud in the interval between them, and drew the conclusion that clouds do not affect the barometric pressure.[34] Later, probably after reading De Saussure's *Essais*, he concluded from this apparent weightlessness that clouds must be made of vesicles of the same specific gravity as the air.[35] He would only hazard a vague guess, not unlike that of De Saussure, on the mechanism by which such vesicles are formed.[36] He continued to believe in vesicles, and in 1791[37] reprimanded the famous Gaspard Monge for maintaining that clouds appear to float because (1) the particles are very small and (2) the affinity of water for air (Monge believed in the solution theory of evaporation) causes an atmosphere to adhere to each droplet.[38] Monge's paper was really quite out of date, and Deluc's strictures were in other particulars quite justified.

3. VISCOSITY COMES IN

We must now go back to about 1745, when Georg Wolfgang Krafft of Tübingen wrote an extensive pamphlet about the subject,[39] in which he gave a number of reasons for his disbelief in the vesicles. But the value of his work, which seems to have remained quite

[32] *Essais sur l'hygrométrie*, pp. 217–18.   [33] See Chapter 8 below.

[34] J. A. Deluc, *Recherches sur les modifications de l'atmosphère*, 2 vol., Geneva 1772, ¶ 672.

[35] Deluc, *Idées sur la météorologie*, 2 vol., London, 1786, & Paris, 1787, ¶ 607.

[36] *Ibid.*, ¶ 609.   [37] Deluc, *Ann. de Chimie* 8 (1791), 86 ff.

[38] Monge, *Ann. de Chimie* 5 (1790), 1–71. Monge invented descriptive geometry.

[39] Krafft, *Cogitationes in experimenta et sententias de vaporum et halituum generatione ac elevatione*. Tübingen, 1745. There is a copy in the library of the *Bundeswetterdienst* at Offenbach-am-Main.

unknown,[40] was more positive; he suggested a better mechanism for the suspension of clouds. After discussing various hypotheses, he goes on:

> One reason may be recommended above all others: that such an extremely small particle, even if it is heavier than air, is able to swim in it for a long time, once it is propelled into it. Pardies[41] did not consider that the air, especially the upper air, is set in continuous motion, the cause of this being the ceaseless action of the sun on its various parts. Nor does he seem to have turned his mind to the almost infinite smallness of the particles that the elementary fire tears away from bodies, nor to the viscosity always present in air, even when it is thin. Thus, every day when the sun shines, we see tiny but yet visible atoms flying hither and thither in the almost still air of some room . . . and ascending too, and remaining a long time in the air, although they are all heavier than the air itself, as is abundantly clear from the fact that they come down again. So too exhalations and vapours will be retained much longer in the upper region of the air, both because they consist of almost infinitely small particles, and because they are sustained by air that is always in motion.[42]

This brings viscosity into the problem. A decade later Franklin brought it in again, but in his own particular manner:[43]

> The atmosphere supposed at rest, a loaded descending particle must act with a force on the particles it passes between, or meets with, sufficient to overcome to some degree their mutual repellency, and push them nearer to each other.
>
> Thus, supposing the particles ABCD (fig. 3.1), and the others near them, to be at the distance caused by their mutual repellency (confined by their common gravity) if A would descend to E, it must pass between B and C. When it comes between B and C, it will be nearer to them than before, and must either have pushed them nearer to F and G, contrary to their mutual repellency, or pass through by a force exceeding its repellency with them. It then approaches D and, to move it out of the way, must act on it with a force sufficient to overcome its

[40] I should not have heard of it except for the reference in the invaluable *Repertorium der deutschen Meteorologie* of Gustav Hellmann (Leipzig, 1883), a bibliography of the utmost importance to every historian of meteorology.

[41] See p. 46 above.   [42] Krafft, *Cogitationes*, p. 43.

[43] Benjamin Franklin, *Phil. Trans.* 55 (1765), 182–92. This paper had been received on June 3, 1756, and forgotten (Royal Society, *Journal Book*).

repellency with the two next lower particles, by which it is kept in its present situation.

Every particle of air, therefore, will bear any load inferior to the force of these repulsions.

Hence the support of fogs, mists, clouds.[44]

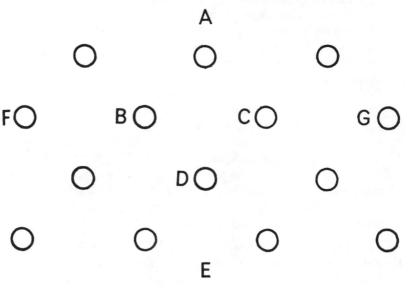

FIG. 3.1. Illustrating Franklin's ideas about the suspension of clouds

This static model is of course Newtonian, and it is likely that Franklin came to adopt it by way of Desaguliers's *A course of experimental philosophy*.[45] It does not seem to have received much attention, and perhaps Franklin did not expect general assent, for he entitled his paper 'Physical and Meteorological Observations, Conjectures, and Suppositions'.

4. BUBBLES AGAIN

I shall now disregard strict chronology and deal briefly with the subsequent history of the vesicle theory. Without neglecting any significant contribution we can make a surprising jump to 1845, and also

[44] *Ibid.*, p. 186.

[45] See I. Bernard Cohen, *Franklin and Newton*. Philadelphia, The American Philosophical Society, 1956, (*Memoirs*, vol. 43), especially Chap. 7.

into the entirely different field of atmospheric optics. In that year, Auguste Bravais, professor of physics at the *École Polytechnique*, assumed that the 'white rainbow' sometimes seen on clouds or fogs opposite the sun, is formed by hollow droplets, and did an elaborate piece of geometrical-optical analysis to demonstrate this.[46] To Bravais this was no mere academic exercise; he believed firmly in these vesicles and considered this the best possible proof of their existence.

Unfortunately for Bravais, Sir George Airy, the Astronomer Royal, had shown in 1836 that the geometrical optical approach simply is not adequate to explain the rainbow, which is an interference phenomenon.[47] As far as the vesicles are concerned, Bravais was effectively answered by F. Raillard in 1857, who, after a consideration of all the available theory and observational evidence, concluded that there is no support whatever from the rainbow for 'the really singular hypothesis of the vesicular state'.[48] The whiteness of the bow follows from the small size of the cloud-droplets, as was demonstrated in detail much later by Pernter.[49] It was also shown by De Tessan[50] that cloud-bows are seldom seen because unless the cloud is very dense and very close to the observer, not enough energy is redirected by the small droplets for a bow to be visible.

Leaving De Tessan's other contributions for the moment, let us keep on with our atmospheric optics. The German physicist R. J. E. Clausius, famous for his work in thermodynamics, unfortunately persuaded himself that the turbidity in the atmosphere had to be vesicular.[51] He went clear back a century to Kratzenstein, in effect, treating atmospheric colours as being those of thin films, and doing a great deal of difficult analysis. Even the blue of the sky was to be produced in this way. He was really quite out of his *métier*, but his

[46] A. Bravais, *J. École royale polytechnique* 18, cahier 30 (1845), 97–122.
[47] This was published in 1838 in *Trans. Cambridge Phil. Soc.* 6 (1838), 379–403. For the history of the rainbow, *see* Carl B. Boyer, *The rainbow from myth to mathematics.* New York & London, Thomas Yoseloff, 1959. Also J. M. Pernter & F. M. Exner, *Meteorologische Optik*, 2nd ed., Vienna & Leipzig, 1922, pp. 527–602.
[48] F. Raillard, *Compt. Rend.* 44 (1857), 1142–44.
[49] See *Meteorologische Optik, ed. cit.*, pp. 565 ff.
[50] *Compt. Rend.* 48 (1859), 905–07; 972–77; 1045–7.
[51] *Ann. der Phys.* 76 (1849), 161–95.

immense authority kept the vesicular hypothesis alive for another twenty-five years, especially in Germany. An adequate job of demolition was done by Kober in 1871[52] and by Budde in 1873,[53] but meanwhile the important textbook of Schmid,[54] relying on Clausius, assumed the vesicular nature of cloud-particles to be proved, and indeed many of the European textbooks adopted the theory quite uncritically.[55] The great chemist Berzelius also lent his immense influence to the theory.[56] Of course, at least after about 1840, few would have wished to argue that the vesicles float because they are full of something lighter than air; it was the existence of the vesicles that was in question.

An attempt to bring the subject into the field of serious experimental science was made by Augustus Waller, who tried to verify by direct observation the presence of vesicles in fogs by repeating De Saussure's observations.[57] He could not see them burst on contact, as De Saussure had claimed to do. In a later paper,[58] Waller began by discussing Kratzenstein's observations of colours in the receiver of an air pump, and pointed out that they are caused by diffraction, not by thin films. He then told how he had caught droplets on films of Canada balsam, turpentine, castor oil, etc., and finally on filaments of spider's web. In every instance the droplets were complete spheres of water, as could be seen from the reflected images of external objects. Similar observations were made on the Brocken forty years later by R. Assmann, the inventor of the psychrometer that bears his name.[59] The theory of vesicles died hard, and in the year of Assmann's article, Charles Ritter thought it necessary to publish a long paper arguing against them, but also in favour of a hypothesis

[52] J. Kober, *Ann. der Phys.* 144 (1871), 395–427.

[53] E. A. Budde, *Ann. der Phys.* 150 (1873), 578–83.

[54] Ernst Erhard Schmid, *Lehrbuch der Meteorologie*, in G. Karsten, ed., *Allgemeine Enzyclopädie der Physik*, [etc.], Vol. 21, Leipzig, 1860.

[55] *E.g.* J. Müller, *Lehrbuch der kosmischen Physik*, Braunschweig, 1856, p. 407. C. S. M. Pouillet, *Eléments de physique expérimentale et de météorologie*. Paris, 1827. 6th ed., Paris, 1853, Vol. 2, 718–19. Pouillet's meteorology, as distinct from his physics, seems to be second-hand for the most part.

[56] J. J. Berzelius, *Traité de chimie*. Transl. J. A. L. Jordan, 8 vol., Paris, 1833, Vol. I, pp. 430–1.

[57] A. Waller, *Phil. Mag.* 28 (1846), 94–105.   [58] *Phil. Trans.* 137 (1847), 23–30.

[59] R. Assmann, *Meteorol. Zeits.* 2 (1885), 41–47.

really derived from De Saussure, in which each droplet drags along an 'atmosphere' of its own.[60]

The most astonishing circumstance about this astonishing theory is that it was vigorously supported by numerous first-class people like Berzelius, Bravais and Clausius, and accepted by others, for example Gay-Lussac, Pouillet and Volta. It is almost equally strange that all these people – and innumerable lesser men – accepted the existence of vesicles in the complete absence of a theory of their formation. Apart from the vague suggestion of 'crystallization' by De Saussure,[61] I only know of one attempt, and that a plainly inadequate one, to provide a mechanism.[62] This was that the 'globule' at first condenses suddenly into a full sphere, but the latent heat of condensation re-vaporizes the part of the water that is least cooled by the environment, namely the interior of the droplet. A fortnight later this author, Lenglet, presented to the *Académie des Sciences* a second note on the subject, which was referred to a *Commission* composed of Babinet and Regnault,[63] and seems to have been quietly dropped.

On the other hand there were several strong denials of the possibility that such vesicles could form in any way whatever. For example De Tessan[64] calculated that for a vesicle to form even in an extremely damp atmosphere (one saturated at 30° C.), all the water molecules in a space 33,000 times as large as the resulting vesicle would have to assemble in precisely the right configuration. Even if it were formed, it could not last, because the internal pressure due to surface tension would cause the air to come through the watery envelope. The effects of surface tension were frequently used in attacks on the vesicular hypothesis; I shall mention only Phillips,[65] Budde,[66] Obermeyer,[67] and König.[68]

[60] Ch. Ritter, *Ann. Soc. Météorol. de France* 33 (1885), 261–90.
[61] See above, p. 51.   [62] Lenglet, *Compt. Rend.* 48 (1859), 1048–9.
[63] *Ibid.*, p. 1116.   [64] *Compt. Rend.* 48 (1859), 1045–7.
[65] Reuben Phillips, *Phil. Mag.* Ser. 4, 5 (1853), 28–30.
[66] E. A. Budde, *Ann. der Phys.* 150 (1873), 579.
[67] A. von Obermeyer, *Zeits. österr. Ges. Meteorol.* 12 (1877), 97–9. Unfortunately he made an egregious numerical error.
[68] W. König, *Meteorol. Zeits.* 5 (1888), 109–10. He pointed out Obermeyer's error.

5. THE SLOW DESCENT

Let us now turn again to other explanations of the suspension of clouds, which we left at the time of Krafft and Franklin. A refreshing breeze of common sense was brought into the subject by John Dalton, famous for his contribution to the atomic theory in chemistry, whom we shall meet again in later chapters. In his first book,[69] published in 1793, we read:

> When a precipitation of vapour takes place, a multitude of exceedingly small drops form a cloud, mist, or fog; these drops, though 800 times denser than the air, at first descend very slowly, owing to the resistance of the air, which produces a greater effect as the drops are smaller[70] . . . From this it appears, that clouds consisting of very small drops may descend very slowly, which is agreeable to observation; if the drops in falling enter into a *stratum* of air capable of imbibing vapour, they may be redissolved, and the clouds not descend at all . . .[71]

In a footnote Dalton acknowledges that these ideas were suggested to him by John Gough, of Kendal.[72] They are an early recognition of the existence of a *condensation level*, although the real implications of the idea could not be understood at the time. Luke Howard used the idea in his celebrated paper on clouds.[73] To account for the flat bases of cumuli, he supposed that vapour rises and is condensed into droplets; these fall until they reach some height at which they again evaporate in the increasing warmth. Unfortunately Howard, who was over-fond of speculation, also ascribed the more-or-less spherical figure of cumuli to the mutual repulsion of all the droplets, which, he said, were electrified; and the various forms of cirrus and cirro-cumulus were considered to be due to different arrangements of electric fields in the upper atmosphere.

[69] John Dalton, *Meteorological observations and essays*, London [1793]. 2nd ed., Manchester & London, 1834. Apart from an appendix the 2nd edition is 'printed *verbatim* from the first, both text and notes'.

[70] He gives an elementary proof of this.

[71] *Meteorological observations and essays* (2nd ed.), p. 134–5.

[72] John Gough was a remarkable blind man who is perhaps best known through references to him by Wordsworth and Coleridge.

[73] Luke Howard, *Phil. Mag.* 16 (1803), 97–107; 344–57; 17 (1803), 5–11.

It was a great step, already taken rather tentatively by Kratzenstein,[74] to realize that the elements of the cloud are constantly falling, and to accept the consequences of this motion. But how fast did they fall? Thomas Young, physician, physicist, and Egyptologist, a man of most extraordinary versatility, provided an answer.[75] With no statement of theory, he asserted that:

> The diameter of a sphere of water, falling at the rate of one inch only in a second, ought to be one six hundred thousandth of an inch . . . but the particles of mist are incomparably larger than this, since they would otherwise be perfectly invisible as separate drops: the least particle, that could be discovered by the naked eye, being such as would fall with a velocity of about a foot in a second, if the air were perfectly at rest.

People are charmed by simple numbers, clearly expressed, and many of them missed the warning in Young's very next sentence:

> But it is very probable that the resistance, opposed to the motion of particles so small, may be considerably greater, than would be expected from a calculation, derived from experiments made on a much larger scale, and their descent consequently much slower.

For example Muncke, writing in or near 1825, quoted the estimate without the warning.[76] Only in 1856 did G. G. Stokes, as a mere incident of an investigation of 'the effect of the internal friction of fluids on the motion of pendulums', furnish a correct theory of the rate of fall of such small bodies as cloud droplets.[77] It turned out that a sphere falling at the rate of one inch a second has about 600 times the diameter supposed by Young. I am inclined to think that Young's statement had a good deal to do with the persistence of the vesicle theory. Berzelius, for example, thought that the vesicles might even have a specific gravity almost equal to that of the air,

> but it is still a mystery to physicists how they remain in the air for days on end; this has no connection with the heating of the lower

[74] See p. 49 above.
[75] Thomas Young, *A course of lectures on natural philosophy* [etc.], 2 vol., London 1807; Vol. I, pp. 711–12.
[76] In Gehler's *Physikalisches Wörterbuch*, Vol. II, p. 655.
[77] *Trans. Cambridge Phil. Soc.* 9 (1856), No. X, p. [51].

layers of the atmosphere, or of the outer parts of the clouds themselves, as some naturalists have thought, for the clouds keep their place during the night also.[78]

Had Berzelius known that even a cloud of droplets might sink only a few hundred feet in a whole night – quite apart from the possibility of the drops evaporating at a certain altitude – he might have felt differently. And of course Berzelius was rather out of his *métier*.

However, his remarks lead us naturally to consider the effect of convection, which he denied. The discovery of convection is generally credited to Benjamin Thompson, Count of Rumford, who indeed was the first to make systematic experiments upon it;[79] but the fact that locally-heated parts of the atmosphere rise, was clearly stated by Franklin in a letter to John Mitchell, F.R.S., dated 29 April 1749, and published in 1751.[80] Franklin writes:

When there is a great heat on the land in a particular region (the sun having shone on it perhaps several days, while the surrounding countries have been screen'd by clouds) the lower air is rarified and rises, the cooler denser air above descends; the clouds in that air meet from all sides, and join over the heated place; and if some are electrified, others not, lightning and thunder succeed, and showers fall. Hence thunder gusts after heats, and cool air after gusts; the water and the clouds that bring it, coming from a higher and therefore a cooler region.[81]

The phenomenon was described more clearly in 1765 by the mathematical physicist Johann Heinrich Lambert, famous for his book on photometry and in many other fields.[82] Lambert first notes that if the earth is assumed flat, a uniform change of temperature over all could not change the height of the barometer, for heat will not change the whole weight of the air. But

---

[78] Berzelius, *Traité de chimie*, I, 431.

[79] Rumford, *On the propagation of heat in fluids*, Part I. London, 1797.

[80] Franklin, *Experiments and observations on Electricity, made in Philadelphia* [etc.], London, 1751, pp. 36–49. On this letter *see* Cohen, *Franklin and Newton*, Philadelphia, 1956, pp. 481 sqq. Franklin called his correspondent 'Mitchel.'

[81] Franklin (1751), p. 46. In the absence of the knowledge that rising air has to cool, this was a good try.

[82] Lambert, *Abh. Akad. München*, II Theil, 3 (1765), 75–182.

If the change of temperature is not general, it is clear that the air will be expanded only where the heat has increased, so that equilibrium in the upper air will be destroyed until the heaped-up air can flow sideways.

This disturbance of the equilibrium causes a circulation of the air, if the heat be increased over a good-sized area of land. For as the air aloft flows from the warmer region into the colder regions that border it, the pressure in the former regions will be increased, and as a result the equilibrium will be disturbed at the bottom. Because of this the lower air will flow towards the warmer region.[83]

This paper is about the measurement of heights with the barometer, and Lambert seems to have had no interest in the meteorological application of this fruitful concept. Such an interest might have made a great change in the history of meteorology, for Lambert was universally respected. As it was, few people can have seen his paper.[84]

It is not very likely that one of these few was Marcellin Ducarla-Bonifas, usually known as Du Carla, who about 1780 published at Geneva a considerable work under the resounding title *Histoire naturelle du monde*. This appeared in parts, of which the seventh was entitled *Des météores locaux*.[85] On pp. 37–8 of this it is made quite clear that whenever the surface is warmer than the air a rising current is produced, and that clouds form in such currents. The idea was familiar to De Saussure,[86] who had read Du Carla and often refers to the *courant ascendant* and its production by heating. We shall go into his views more fully in Chapter five.

But before much use could be made of this idea, it had to be made clear that ascending air *necessarily* becomes cooler, and the mathematical proof of this was given by Poisson in 1823.[87] This idea was not immediately applied to meteorology, however, and the first man to print anything of any consequence about its implications was

[83] *Ibid.*, pp. 100–1.
[84] The argument was repeated in his *Pyrometrie oder vom Maase des Feuers und der Wärme*, Berlin 1779, p. 229.
[85] Du Carla, [*Histoire naturelle du monde*], Septième Cahier. Des météores locaux. Genève, chez Du Villard Fils & Nouffer, 1780. This seems to be extremely rare; I have not found a copy in the BM or the BN, but there is one at Geneva.
[86] *Essais sur l'hygrométrie*, p. 261 and *passim*.
[87] S. D. Poisson, *Ann. de Chim.* 23 (1823), 337–52.

the American James Pollard Espy.[88] By 1850 Espy felt able to dispose
of the old question about the suspension of clouds in these terms:

> It is not necessary to inquire, as is frequently done, by what power are
> the clouds suspended in the air, unless it can be shown that they are
> suspended, of which I think there is no probability ... We have every
> reason to believe ... that the particles of cloud begin to fall through
> the air ... as soon as they are separated from the up-moving column of
> air, by means of which the cloud was formed.[89]

[88] See Chapter VIII.
[89] J. P. Espy, 'Second and third reports on meteorology to the Secretary of the
Navy.' U.S. Congress, 31st Congress, 1st Session (Senate). *Ex. Doc. No. 39*, Washington 1850, p. 33.

Chapter Four

THE VARIATIONS OF THE BAROMETER

He could not but observe a manifest connection between the alterations of the mercurial station, and the course of the winds and weather; but could not fix in his mind any certain rules of indication, but rather the contrary, viz. that events failed as often as corresponded· with the ordinary expectation.

Roger North, LIFE OF THE RT. HON.
FRANCIS NORTH, BARON GUILFORD [etc.]
London, 1742, p. 295.

1. THE PUZZLE

In February 1645, less than a year after the 'Torricellian experiment' was first described, Cardinal Giovanni Carlo de'Medici had several Torricellian tubes set up at Rome and kept under observation for some time. It was found that the changes in the level of the mercury could not be correlated with the observed changes of temperature and humidity, so that 'the height of the mercury is not changed by the alteration of the air around it, but by that of all the air in a broad region'.[1] Thus began the long attempt to find a scientific basis for forecasting the weather, and the search for a rational explanation of the irregular variations of the barometer.

The very earliest observations of the tube provided one of the most fascinating and baffling of all the puzzles in Nature's box. For it was at once discovered that the mercury usually stands at its greatest height in fine weather, and at its lowest on the rainiest days, when the air is most full of 'vapours and exhalations' and therefore obviously 'heaviest'.

[1] Emmanuel Maignan, *Cursus philosophicus concinnatus ex notissimis cuique principiis* [etc.], 4 vol. (paged as one), Toulouse, 1653, p. 1898. For more detail see my *The history of the barometer*, Baltimore, 1964, pp. 33–4.

One senses that this was an enormous surprise, and even a disappointment; Nature was not playing fair. In or about 1654 Pierre Gassendi, the philosopher who re-introduced Epicurus to the west, was writing as follows:

> ... when the sky is clear and north winds blowing, the mercury in the tube will always remain higher than when the sky is covered and the winds blow from the south. But when the sky is purer the weight of their air *ought to be* far less than when it is turbid, and so press more lightly on the stagnant mercury [*i.e.*, that in the barometer cistern], and in consequence the mercury ought to be raised less high, and to remain so in the tube.[2]

Desperate cases demand desperate remedies; Gassendi prescribes one:

> The cause of this seems to be that in fair weather, just as in the cold, those vapours do not emerge from the earth as they do in hotter, cloudier weather. [He goes on to explain that some of the corpuscles that make up these vapours press upwards instead of downwards.] The corpuscles of the clouds are of this kind; indeed you would not see them actually suspended unless there were a force carrying them up and sustaining them, just as thistledown is carried up and flies through the air.[3]

Presumably the corpuscles, pushing upwards, sustain part of the weight of the air. This idea seems to have been put forward once again, by Nicolaus Hartsoecker in 1696.[4] Perhaps Boyle had been reading Gassendi when he performed the twenty-ninth of his experiments with the air pump to see if 'positive levity' – a Peripatetic shibboleth – was responsible for the rise of vapours. He opened a vessel containing a 'fuming liquor' under the exhausted receiver of his air pump and found that the fumes ran down the sides of the vessel.[5]

So something better had to be found. The various theories that

---

[2] Gassendi, *Opera omnia in sex tomos divisa*. Leyden, 1658, Vol. I, p. 216. The italics are mine.

[3] *Ibid.*

[4] Hartsoecker, *Principles de physique*. Paris 1696. (Summarized in *Acta Eruditorum*, (1697), 1–5.)

[5] Robert Boyle, *New experiments physico-mechanicall touching the spring of the air, and its effects* [etc.]. Oxford, 1660, pp. 217–23.

were put forward permit of a rough classification, but we shall treat the first half-century after the invention of the barometer very nearly chronologically.

2. THE FIRST FIFTY YEARS

As soon as the barometer was available, indeed long before it had received its name,[6] it was realized that it would be a good idea to have simultaneous observations at various places – 'synoptic' observations as we now call them. In a letter dated 13 December 1647, Descartes tried to arrange such observations with Mersenne;[7] and ten years later Ferdinand II, Grand Duke of Tuscany and founder of the *Accademia del Cimento*, began the establishment of a network of ten stations.[8] In England, John Beale was trying to establish stations in the 1660's.[9] We are told of his enthusiasm:

> The said Doctor is so much pleased with the discovery already made by the help of this instrument, that he thinks it to be one of the most wonderful that ever was in the world, if we speak of strangeness, and just wonder, and of philosophical importance, separate from the interest of lucre. For (saith he, in one of his letters) who could ever expect, that we men should find an art, to weigh all the air that hangs over our heads, in all the changes of it, and, as it were, to weigh, and to distinguish by weight, the winds and the clouds? And who did believe, that by palpable evidence, we should be able to prove, the serenest air to be the most heavy, and the thickest air, and when darkest clouds hang neerest to us, ready to dissolve, or dropping, then to be lightest . . .[10]

Beale does not seem to have hazarded a guess as to the reason; but the Savilian Professor of Geometry at Oxford, John Wallis, had no such inhibitions, even if no more information.[11] He found the quicksilver to rise 'in thick foggy weather', and ascribed this 'to the heaviness of the vapours in the air'.[12] It also rose in sunshiny weather;

[6] In 1663, at the hands of Boyle. See W. E. K. Middleton, *The history of the barometer*, Baltimore, 1964, p. 71.

[7] Middleton, *History*, p. 46. [8] *Ibid.*, p. 61.

[9] Anon. [Probably by Henry Oldenburg], *Phil. Trans.* 1 (1666), 153–9.

[10] *Ibid.*, p. 155. [11] J. Wallis, *Phil. Trans.* 1 (1666), 166–71.

[12] *Ibid.*, p. 170. Radiation fogs in inland regions are characteristic of anticyclonic weather.

partly, he thought, because of the vapours raised by the sun, and partly because the heat increases the elasticity of the air. But 'in rainy weather, it useth to fall (of which the reason is obvious, because the air is lightened, by so much as falls) . . . For windy weather, I find it generally to fall; and that more universally, and more discernably, than upon rain: (which I attribute to the winds moving the air collaterally, and thereby not suffering it to press so much directly downwards: the like of which we see in swimming, &c.) And I have never found it lower than in high winds.'[13]

Here we have four of the trails that were to bedevil the scientific detectives for more than a century: (1) heavy vapours, (2) the idea that the 'elasticity' of the air could be independent of the pressure due to its weight, (3) the effect of the fall of rain, and (4) the supposed effect of wind. Not many later writers were as eclectic as Wallis.

Giovanni Alfonso Borelli, one of the most active members of the *Accademia del Cimento*, managed at various times to adopt two of these ideas, and another of his own. Borelli was, in a way, the first working meteorologist, for he made systematic observations of the thermometer, barometer, wind, and weather on the orders of his patron the Grand Duke Ferdinand II, whom he describes as 'a very keen explorer of the operations of Nature'[14] – an estimate which posterity has confirmed.

The idea which seems to be original with Borelli was apparently that the particles of moisture in the clouds somehow rest on each other and support part of the weight of the air above. The evidence for the existence of this idea is that there is a letter dated 15 December 1657 from Prince Leopold, the clever and scientifically-minded brother of Ferdinand II, in which such an idea is opposed.[15] The pertinent sentence of this letter may be translated as follows:

[13] *Ibid.*, p. 170.

[14] G. A. Borelli, *De motionibus naturalibus a gravitate pendentibus*. Regio Julio, 1670, p. 238. The idea of a meteorological network was probably due to Viviani (see Florence, *Bibl. Naz.*, ms. Gal. 283, fol. 35ʳ–36ᵛ, letter from Borelli to Viviani, 11 Jan. 1658).

[15] This letter is at Florence, *Bibl. Naz.*, ms. Gal. 282, fol. 2ʳ–3ᵛ. The last figure of the year is doubtful, but probably a 7.

I still doubt whether those minute particles of moisture, which are in the clouds and descend little by little, either as rain or fog or in some other form, and come down to earth, can produce the same effect as a solid body, the lowest parts that touch the earth supporting the upper parts, as if the cloud were like a brush, for example.

The idea seems more primitive than the one revealed in a correspondence between Prince Leopold and Borelli in March 1660. I have been able to find only Borelli's part of the exchange; but the Prince's reception of the idea is quite easy to deduce, as we shall see.

Borelli reported to the Prince from Pisa on March 5, 1660, that the mercury in the Torricellian tube was exceptionally high that morning, much higher than he had ever observed it in three years; '20 degrees' higher, in fact. It appears from a second letter that the usual height of the barometer is about 460 of these degrees, so that the barometer must have been very high indeed. This freak of nature (*strauaganza*), says Borelli,

> shows that the air lying above the level of Pisa is excessively and extraordinarily greater in weight that it has been at other times, because of the mixture of other material, vaporous, aqueous, or earthy, with it. We shall see whether some extraordinarily excessive and abundant rain follows such an unexpected phenomenon. Or, if the material is not aqueous, and does not get dissipated by the winds, we shall see whether perchance something of the kind follows, that usually precedes comets.[16] I know very well, Your Highness, that a thousand accidents may intervene to disturb the process about which I have made conjectures, so that if the said effect does not happen, this will not succeed in controverting the cause I have supposed, namely that at various times the air may become more, or less heavy, according to the ascent of terrestrial particles. This is so solidly proved and established, that it has no need of confirmation by the outcome of the above conjecture, which I have thought well to impart to Your Highness, in order to give you the opportunity of philosophizing about it.[17]

The Prince and the Grand Duke quite evidently had their own ideas on the subject, and Leopold communicated them to Borelli

[16] In 1660 the precise rôle of comets in the economy of nature was sufficiently in doubt to justify such a statement.

[17] Florence, *Bibl. Naz.*, ms. Gal. 276, fol. 10ʳ-11ʳ.

almost at once, in a letter that I have been unable to find. Fortunately the excellent suggestion made by Leopold in this lost letter is clearly indicated in Borelli's next, which is dated Pisa, 16 March 1660, and begins as follows:

> In order to obey the command of the Most Serene Grand Duke and Your Highness, I am answering Your Highness's question. With your usual acuteness and perspicacity, you point out that the continuation of a strong wind could accumulate a large quantity of air above the level of Pisa and its surroundings; that the weight of the air may well be increased in this way, so that the quicksilver may be caused to rise in the tube; but that it is not at all necessary that the prognostications that I made should turn out correct: *i.e.* of copious rain, or else of something such as appears before a comet.[18]

Borelli was probably the first forecaster who ever issued a poor forecast on scientific principles. He goes on to point out that he had hedged in his previous letter in his reference to the 'thousand accidents' that might disturb his supposed process, and that these words of his were 'general enough to include the case considered by Your Highness'. At this point he pulls himself together and continues:

> But in order not to appear to have spoken with such caution and artifice as to have a sure way out in any event, it is my duty to enlarge a little further on this matter, and to make known the reasons why I doubt that the winds are able to produce such an effect.[19]

The 'little further' ran to five pages, and I shall not reproduce it here. His doubts were quantitative, which is to his credit. He could not believe that air could be piled up to the extent of a twentieth of the usual amount, especially when it is considered that the air becomes less dense aloft. Nor could he believe that such an accumulation could endure for several days, for, as he points out, a water wave cannot maintain itself in one place for a moment. So he has to return to his ideas of heavy vapours and exhalations.

Leopold and Ferdinand were far ahead of their time. That they should have made such a sound guess can only increase our very considerable respect for the scientific acumen of these Tuscan noble-

[18] *Ibid.*, fol. 12ʳ.   [19] *Ibid.*, fol. 12ᵛ.

men. Even after an ample discount for the desire of courtiers to please, it is clear that they were well able to hold their own with their cleverest 'natural philosophers'.

Ten years later Borelli hit upon a different idea, quite like one of Wallis's explanations. He believed he had noticed that before a long and continuous rain the barometer is usually high, but that during the rain it falls, sometimes as much as an inch, at Pisa. To explain the fall he performed, or possibly imagined, an experiment in which a barometer is placed with its cistern at the bottom of a tall jar of oil. Next he floats a vessel, partly full of sand, on the oil, and the mercury rises because the oil-level is raised. Then he pours out the sand, which descends through the oil. There will be no change in the barometer until the sand has reached the bottom of the vessel, when the mercury will fall. He applies this result to the atmosphere, saying that when the rain has reached the earth the barometer will go down.[20] However, he recognizes that there are other causes of its changes, and in particular one cannot reason that rain is to be expected just because the barometer is high.

Naturally enough, the problem of the variations of the barometer received a good deal of attention at the hands of the Royal Society during these years. The discussion of it was particularly lively during January 1677–8, and again a year later, in February 1678–9. At the meeting on 3 January 1677–8, Robert Hooke was again speculating that a high barometer must mean that 'exhalations' have been added to the air, and so:

> By these ways he explained the phenomena of the great gravity of the air upon the long blowing of an eastwardly, and the lightness of it upon the blowing of a southwardly wind; the air in the one coming over a vast tract of land, and so taking up into itself great quantities of exhalations, which remain suspended and mixt with it by reason of their congruity; and the other blowing over a great space of sea, which affords a less quantity of parts disposed to make air.[21]

[20] *De motionibus*, pp. 241–4.
[21] Thomas Birch, *The History of the Royal Society*, 4 vols., London, 1756–7. Vol. III, p. 371. In the *Micrographia* (1665), Preface, sig. C2, Hooke had already connected high pressure, easterly winds, and 'earthy particles'.

Why the terrestrial exhalations should be more 'congruous' than the marine ones is hard to see; but at any rate Hooke had noticed the frequent association of easterly weather with high pressure in southeast England. Such weather in winter is often overcast, which may have seemed to support this explanation.

At the meeting of 13 February 1678/9, it was pointed out that the mere expansion or contraction of the whole column of air by heat or cold would not change the pressure; and it was therefore supposed that a higher pressure could only be caused by the addition of air at the top of the atmosphere, or else by something from the earth that changed the specific gravity of parts of the air. The discussion evidently made a great impression on Thomas Henshaw, the Vice-president, who moved enthusiastically – and optimistically –

> that the substance of this discourse might be drawn up; and that the whole theory might be fully explained, as soon as possible; the barometer being become an instrument of general use, and the causes and reasons thereof being very commonly debated amongst the learned.[22]

On February 20 Hooke again referred to the necessity of adding or taking away something; the something could be vapours lighter or heavier than air. Finally on 27 there was a discussion of 'whether vapours ascending or rain descending through the air change the pressure of the air beneath them with their whole weight'.[23] This suggests that someone had been reading Borelli's book, which was and still is in the library of the Society.[24]

The next contribution emphasized changes in the specific gravity of the air as the primary cause of the variations in the height of the mercury. It was by George Garden, a Doctor at Aberdeen; and shows remarkable ingenuity and considerable powers of observation,[25] in spite of its rickety base. Garden supposed that the specific

[22] Birch, III, p. 462. Thomas Henshaw was one of the charter Fellows, but more distinguished in the Law than in Science.

[23] *Ibid.*, p. 466.

[24] On the half-title of the copy in the Royal Society's Library is written 'Liber exhibitus Regia [*sic*] Societati nomine Authoris d. 15 junij 1671'.

[25] Garden, *Phil. Trans.* 15 (1685), 991–1001.

gravity of the air is greater than that of the vapours when the barometer is high, less when it is low. Therefore, by the laws of hydrostatic equilibrium, the vapours rise less when the barometer is low, and Garden notes that with a high barometer and a clear sky the distant hills are usually indistinct, but when it is low they are clearly seen. The fact that rain and snow 'usually fall out only when the mercury subsides a little' confirmed him in his conjecture that the changes in the specific gravity of the air are the determining factor.

This idea had enough vitality to be repeated by Musschenbroek half a century later.[26] While it is not quite pertinent to our discussion, it is of interest to note that Garden also explained winds on the basis of hydrostatic equilibrium:

> the air's gravity is not alike chang'd throughout the whole atmosphere in an instant, but . . . the mercury may have subsided in the baroscope and consequently the air become lighter, at London, for example, when there is no such change observ'd at Paris or Edinburg.[27]

This appeared only a year before the famous paper on the trade winds by Edmond Halley.[28] Garden admitted that he could not account for the changes in specific gravity of the atmosphere, and put forward a few speculations, including the idea of a more subtle fluid 'of a far greater pressure than air . . . and in which the air seems as it were to float'.[29] Certainly cold and heat influence the weight of the air; he has observed the mercury to rise with northerly, and fall with southerly winds. It seems to me that Garden came close to an understanding of large-scale advection but could not quite reach it. His paper was followed in the pages of the *Philosophical Transactions* by a rambling discussion, probably requested by the editor, from John Wallis,[30] who had forgotten his earlier enthusiasms, and while – reasonably enough – he objected to the 'subtle matter', he ends up by wondering whether most of the barometric

[26] P. van Musschenbroek, *Essai de physique* [etc.]. Leyden, 1739, p. 737.
[27] Garden (1685), p. 996.   [28] *Phil. Trans.* 16 (1686), 153–68.
[29] Garden, 1685, p. 997. For a possible source of this idea, see my *History of the barometer*, pp. 78–81.
[30] *Phil. Trans.* 15 (1685), 1002–14.

changes we observe are not really due to the effects of heat and cold on the air and water contained in the mercury!

Besides the trade-winds paper, Halley published another one in 1686, mainly devoted to establishing a formula for barometric hypsometry, but also speculating about the relation of the barometer to the weather.[31] In this paper Halley adopts the theory of hydrostatic equilibrium between the air and the vapours, but with an addition to explain why the barometer is often low in calm weather *before* rain:

> the air being light, the vapours are no longer supported thereby, being become specifically heavier than the medium in which they floated; so that they descend towards the earth, and in their fall meeting with other aqueous particles, they incorporate together and forme little drops of rain.[32]

How wide one might throw the net in the attempt to catch the elusive explanation is shown in the following paragraph from the year 1690:

> On the evening of November 28, Mr. De la Hire observed that the mercury of the barometer, which had been at a height of 28 inches, had descended in a very short time to 26 inches 10 lines. The wind was extremely violent at the time. Mr. Varignon said that this could result from the wind breaking the parallel columns of the air.[33]

It would be interesting to know what Pierre Varignon, a mathematician of some distinction, meant by *colomnes collaterales*; perhaps we may get a hint from the fact that Wallis used the word *collaterally* in the passage quoted above.[34] In spite of 'Pascal's principle' and Boyle's experiments, people could not help thinking of an actual column of air pressing on the mercury in the barometer cistern.

Indeed, the problem was so intractable that some authors, like Bernardino Ramazzini of Modena, had to reassure themselves that the mercury really is held up by the weight of the atmosphere. He

---

[31] E. Halley, *Phil. Trans.* 16 (1686), 104–16.   [32] *Ibid.*, p. 111.

[33] (*. . . pouvoit venir de ce que le vent rompt les colomnes collaterales de l'air*). *Histoire de l'Académie Royale des Sciences depuis son éstablissement en 1666 jusqu'à 1699.* 11 vol., Paris, 1733; Vol. 2, p. 87.

[34] Page 66.

found it difficult to explain how the air could be lighter when rain is imminent or even when it is falling, but heavier when the weather had cleared; it is as if one would assert that a woman is heavier after the birth of her baby than when she is pregnant![35]

Ramazzini has recourse to a theory that there are 'earthy, saline, and nitrous exhalations' in the air, which on the approach of rain, being rendered heavier – presumably by absorbing humidity – fall to the ground, and leave the atmosphere lighter. When fine weather comes back these particles are dried out and carried into the air again, especially by the north wind.

These nitrous exhalations are probably the 'nitro-aerial salts' of John Mayow, an Oxford physiologist.[36] Mayow insisted that the air is full of these salts, which are necessary for combustion and for respiration, and in fact perform just those services that oxygen was found to render when it was isolated a century later. They also perform a good many more, of which we have space to mention only one: Mayow believed that the elasticity of the air arises from the nitro-aerial salts. For when a candle is burned in a bottle up-ended in a pan of water, exhausting the salts in the air, the water rises in the bottle.

Guerlac has shown[37] that this theory had its origin at least as early as 1604, and in another paper[38] makes it very probable that the invention of gunpowder, with the inevitable observation that its explosion looks and sounds very like lightning and thunder, lay behind the theory. The chemical explanation of these 'fiery meteors' lasted a long time, in fact until the middle of the eighteenth century. Nothing could show better how seriously the theory was taken than the following quotation from the paper presented by Isaac Newton to the Royal Society on December 9, 1675:[39]

[35] B. Ramazzini, *Ephemerides barometricae Mutinenses anni MDC.XCIV, una cum disquisitione causae ascensus & descensus mercurii in Torricelliana fistula* [etc.]. Modena, 1695, p. XXVIII.

[36] John Mayow, *Tractatus quinque medico-physici* [etc.]. Oxford, 1674.

[37] Henry Guerlac, *Actes 7ᵉ Congrès Int. Hist. Sci.*, 1953, pp. 332–49.

[38] Guerlac, *Isis* 45 (1954), 243–55. More recently A. G. Debus (*Isis* 55 (1964), 43–61) has shown that these ideas go back to Paracelsus.

[39] Newton, 'An Hypothesis explaining the Properties of Light, discoursed of in my several Papers. *In* Birch, *History of the Royal Society*, III, 250–60.

. . . so may the gravitating attraction of the earth be caused by the continual condensation of some other such like aetherial spirit, not of the main body of phlegmatic aether, but of something very thinly and subtilly diffused through it, perhaps of an unctuous or gummy, tenacious, and springy nature, and bearing much the same relation to aether, which the vital aerial spirit, requisite for the conservation of flame and vital motions, does to air.[40]

But let us return to Ramazzini's book. He quotes a letter from J.B.Boccabadati, the Duke of Modena's 'chief engineer', who thought that the air is lighter in times of rain, because then the heat attenuates water into vapours which require more space, being agitated, and so constitute a mixture (*concretum*) of air and vapour that is lighter than air alone. Here, of course, is one of the clues to the puzzle, and it seemed such an unlikely one that Ramazzini paid it no particular attention, but simply followed it by another theory by Francesco Torti, like himself a professor at Modena, that when the vapours start to condense and fall they no longer weigh as part of the air. Ramazzini preferred his own theory of the nitrous exhalations.

This got him into an argument, not always polite and in retrospect, I am afraid, rather dull, with Günther Christoph Schelhammer, physician-in-chief to the Duke of Gottorp in Schleswig-Holstein. This was conducted through Lucas Schroek, president of the *Academia Naturae Curiosorum*, and later published.[41] It is unnecessary to go into detail about this; I shall confine myself to mentioning Schelhammer's two theories, apparently independent, and both surely among the curiosities of science. The first was the astonishing idea that the mercury *in the cistern* of the barometer will float higher in the denser (*i.e.* moist and cloudy) air than in dry air, so that the mercury in the tube will have to descend. This idea was arrived at by a misinterpretation of what happens when the cistern of a barometer is submerged in water. By another travesty of hydrostatics he concludes that rain or cloud sustains the weight of that part

[40] *Ibid.*, pp. 250–1.
[41] Schelhammer, *De motu mercurii in tubo Torricilliano* [sic] *epistola. Accessit altera ejusdem argumenti Bernhardi Ramazzini . . . Itemque tertia, sive ejusdem Schelhameri ad objectiones Ramazzinianas.* Kiel, 1699.

of the atmosphere above it, or at least some of the weight, so that when these hydrometeors occur the barometer goes down.

Ramazzini, who was a better scientist and a much better writer than Schelhammer, made short work of these arguments, but Schelhammer's rebuttal, even more confusing than his exposition, shows him still convinced that he has won.

Much later, long after he had moved to Padua, Ramazzini gave up the 'nitrous salts' theory in order to adopt an idea suggested by Leibnitz, which will be dealt with below. This revived the controversy with Schelhammer, and the great Leibnitz was called in to show the Duke's physician the error of his ways.[42, 43, 44]

For the remainder of this chapter it will be clearer to adopt a classification of the explanations of the variations of the barometer, and I shall deal with them under the following headings: the supposed weightlessness of falling drops, the effects of wind, explanations based on advection, and finally a few miscellaneous theories.

3. THE WEIGHTLESSNESS OF RAINDROPS

In 1670 Borelli demonstrated by a logical argument that liquid in free fall is weightless,[45] and also described an experiment[46] which looks superficially as if it were designed to illustrate this theorem, but it is not; for the sand falling through the oil was plainly not in a state of free fall. We have also noted that the question of the weightlessness of falling drops had been considered by the Royal Society in 1678/9, and that the effect had been again suggested by Torti about 1695.

It seems likely that about 1700 Ramazzini, perhaps inspired by

[42] Ramazzini, *Ephem. Acad. Nat. Cur.*, Cent. I & II, appendix, pp. 92–8; 106. Frankfurt & Leipzig, 1712 (The article is dated Padua, June 1, 1710).

[43] Schelhammer, *Ibid.*, pp. 98–105. This time Ramazzini published the controversy, as *Ephemerides barometricae, Mutinae olim editae a Bernhardo Ramazzini . . . nunc Patavii recusae cum tota controversia . . . cum D.[omino] C. Gunthero Schelhamero, . . . Accedit nova epistola ejusdem Ramazzini, cum solutione problematis inter ipsos agitati ex invento G. C. Leibnitii*. Padua, 1710.

[44] Leibnitz, *Ephem. Acad. Nat. Cur.*, Cent. III & IV, appendix, pp. 49–51. Nürnberg, 1715.

[45] Borelli, *De motionibus*, p. 53.   [46] See p. 69 above.

his colleague Torti, had written to Leibnitz concerning the problem; at any rate the latter wrote to him from Hanover describing as experiment that seemed to settle the question.[47] The experiment is as follows: Let a tall vessel of water be hung from a balance, with a hollow body of some heavy material floating on the water. Bring the balance to equilibrium. Now if a hole be opened in the hollow body, it will fill with water and sink to the bottom. While it is descending, Leibnitz says, the equilibrium will be disturbed, because during this time the water is not sustaining it, so that it will not be weighed by the balance. Now compare the vessel of water to the atmosphere, the falling body to the raindrops, and the mercury in the barometer to the weight at the other end of the beam. In fine weather 'the drops of water are so finely divided and dispersed in the air that they cannot descend, any more than the buttery particles of milk before separation'.[48] The mercury can begin to descend some time before the rain falls to the ground, because the drops begin to form before they reach us.

After his move to Padua, Ramazzini goes on, he had many other concerns and had not thought about the problem until recently. He seems to have completely abandoned the theory of nitrous salts. During the Christmas holidays, he and Giovanni Gratiano had done the experiment suggested by Leibnitz, with a very good balance, varying it only by hanging a heavy body in the water by a fine thread, also attached to the balance arm, and cutting the thread. The experiment, repeated several times, always succeeded. He realizes that this does not explain why the barometer sometimes falls without rain, but he is sure nevertheless that Schelhammer will rejoice with him that solution of their common problem begins to emerge.

But Schelhammer, far from rejoicing, refuses to believe that the heavy body suspended in the water is in the same situation as the raindrops; and he is bothered – reasonably enough – by the very

[47] Ramazzini (1712), p. 94. This letter and the experiment seem to have come to light only when Ramazzini wrote to the Academy in 1710, but I am not certain that there was no earlier publication of the experiment.
[48] *Ibid.*, p. 95.

early warning of rain, even one or more days, given by the barometer. He also objects that Ramazzini's way of doing the experiment
is different from that suggested by Leibnitz.

In his final contribution to the controversy, Leibnitz tried to show
Schelhammer (1) that the two ways of doing the experiment are
equivalent, (2) that the heavy bodies press on the water just as
floating vapour presses on the air, (3) that it takes the drops some time
to come down, and that they can be retarded or dissipated by a wind
aloft or some other cause, and (4) that this dissipation can even
completely prevent the rain. He admitted that barometric changes
can be due to other causes, such as great storms, but believed that
his explanation was the main one.

This ended the controversy for the time, and in a year or two
both protagonists were dead, but Leibnitz's experiment continued
to engender more heat than light.

There is no doubt whatever that the experiment, either in
Ramazzini's variation or in Leibnitz's form, is bound to succeed,
though the two experiments are not, in fact, theoretically equivalent,
and indeed Ramazzini's has not even a remote similarity to what
happens in the atmosphere. The fallacy of applying either experiment to the atmosphere can best be seen by considering that drops
of water of any size, from the most minute cloud droplet to the
largest raindrop, are always falling through the air at their limiting
speed. This is the speed at which the resistance of the air to the downward motion of the drop becomes equal to the weight of the drop
minus that of the volume of air that it displaces. By Newton's third
law, this resistance will appear as a downward force at the bottom
of the atmosphere. But the coagulation of smaller drops into larger
ones will not alter this force – or the barometric pressure – in the
least, even though the larger drops fall much faster than the tiny particles of cloud. As we saw in Chapter Three, it was not until the nineteenth century that the apparent suspension of clouds was understood.

Thus Leibnitz's suggestion has no validity whatever. Unfortunately it was reported by Fontenelle in the annual 'History' of the
Paris Academy for 1711 as if it were the voice of God.[49] At first,

[49] *Hist. Acad. Roy. Sci. Paris* (1711), 3–6.

nobody seems to have dared to disagree with its theoretical basis, though the quantitative adequacy of the effect was immediately called into question by one Giacopo Placentini[50] at Ramazzini's own University, who noted that rainfall measurements (in France) have shown only seventeen to twenty inches of rain in a whole year, yet the mercury can suddenly descend an inch, and an inch of mercury weighs as much as $13\frac{1}{2}$ inches of water. J. J. d'Ortous de Mairan also believed that the effect would be small, while agreeing with the principle.[51]

The first to disagree thoroughly seems to have been J. T. Desaguliers, who wrote a paper *ad hoc* in 1717,[52] reasoning correctly that as soon as a falling body attains its final speed, equilibrium will be restored. This ought to have settled the matter, and might have done so but for the tremendous reputation of Leibnitz; yet we find S. C. Hollmann in 1749 opposing the idea because, he said, the experiment is unnatural, and also on the basis of the long time that often elapses between the fall of pressure and the rain.[53] And in 1772 Deluc felt it necessary to demolish the hypothesis once and for all, in a very extensive argument of which only one or two paragraphs are really effective and none very clear.[54] It is not surprising that Nikolaus von Beguelin, the meteorologist of the Berlin Academy, should have declined[55] to abandon the theory of Leibnitz, in whom the Academy had, after all, a vested interest; it is doubtful whether he understood the arguments of Deluc.

4. THE EFFECTS OF WIND ON THE BAROMETER

We saw the Paris Academy speculating in 1690 on the effect of strong winds on the barometer. After that time there were a number of

[50] G. Placentini, *De barometro dissertationes duae*. Padua 1711. Summarized in *Acta Eruditorum* (1711), 495–9, from which my information is taken.

[51] De Mairan, *Dissertation sur les variations du baromètre, qui a remporté le Prix à l'-Académie Royale des Belles Lettres, Sciences & Arts de Bordeaux*. Bordeaux, 1715, pp. 22–23.

[52] Desaguliers, *Phil. Trans.* 30 (1717), 570–79.

[53] Hollmann, S. C., *Phil. Trans.* 46 (1749), 101–10.

[54] Deluc, *Modifications*, ¶ 166–92.

[55] Beguelin, *Nouv, Mém. Acad. Berlin* (1774), 128–9.

other speculations along several different lines, and it might be pertinent to classify these. In the first place there was Varignon's idea, apparently that a strong wind somehow prevented the pressure of the air from acting fully on the mercury in the cistern of the barometer. Next there was the belief that rapid horizontal motion diminishes the weight of a moving body. It was also widely believed that contrary winds blowing to or from a certain region might collide and make the air denser, or alternatively leave a slight vacuum between them. Finally winds might have a vertical component upwards or downwards.

It may be well to make a special note at this point for those readers who are completely familiar with the relations between the wind and the distribution of barometric pressure that are now a commonplace to users of weather maps. The knowledge of these relations dates from the middle of the nineteenth century, and is not our concern here. In this section we are dealing only with the supposed physical effects of the motion of air on the readings of the barometer.

At the beginning of the period that we are considering, Leibnitz wrote in French from Hanover on 26 February 1700, evidently to someone at the Paris Academy, emphasizing the effect of wind in producing barometric changes. 'The air will be . . . sustained by violent winds, and particularly by a wind which goes away from the earth as it moves, and tends, in a sense, upwards.'[56] It is necessary to avoid any confusion between the upward currents caused by convection, not recognized at that time, and the upward component of strong winds, as postulated by Leibnitz.

People were impressed by the fact that in western Europe the barometer was normally higher with northerly and easterly winds than when the wind was from the south and west. A clever and well-argued attempt to account for this was made at about this time by Johannis Cruegerus of Jena in a dissertation[57] of much more value than most of those emanating from the German universities of this

[56] G. W. Leibnitz, *Opera omnia . . . nunc primum collecta, in classes distributa . . . studio L. Dutens* [etc.]. 6 vol., Geneva, 1768; Vol. II, part 2, p. 80.
[57] *Dissertatio academica de barometris.* Jena 1701.

period. The idea is simple. Starting from the fact of the existence of the prevailing westerlies, which he considers to be established, he says:

> Now if the wind blows to our land from north or east or some region between these, it will always have against it the constant wind coming from the opposite direction, and therefore the air around us must of necessity be accumulated, condensed, and made heavier, so that its weight, acting on the mercury, makes this ascend. On the other hand if the south or west wind, or one from some intermediate direction, reigns in our country, the constant wind will be added to it, so that it will pull down the heap of congested air, and rarer or lighter air will flow into this place, taking a great weight off the mercury, which will be able to descend a long way.[58]

At about the same time, that valiant experimenter Francis Hauksbee was misled by the oscillations of the barometer in gusty winds now usually referred to as 'pumping', and caused by the dynamic effect of the wind on the pressure in the imperfectly closed room in which the barometer is placed. This is an artificial phenomenon that really has no relation to anything occurring in the free atmosphere, but it was, of course, noticed that on days when the barometer was falling rapidly the wind was often very strong. Hauksbee, following his bent, devised an elaborate apparatus in which a rapid current of air could be passed over a barometer cistern in a closed box. To make things more certain, a tube three feet long connected this to another similar box containing the cistern of another barometer. It so happened that the mechanical arrangement and relative sizes of the inlet and outlet tubes caused the pressure to drop.[59] He might just as easily have produced the opposite effect, as was pointed out later by Christian von Wolff.[60] It is not entirely beside the point to note that Wolff, a first-class man whose services

---

[58] *Ibid.*, pp. 46–47.

[59] Francis Hauksbee, *Physico-mechanicall experiments on various subjects* [etc.]. London, 1709, p. 89. The rather elaborate apparatus is illustrated in Plate 5 of the book.

[60] Wolff, *Allerhand nützliche Versuche, dadurch zu genauer Erkäntniss der Natur und Kunst der Weg gebahnet wird* [etc.] 2nd ed., Halle, 1745–7; Vol. II, pp. 108–9.

to meteorology have been somewhat neglected,[61] had suggested in 1709 that the wind blows from a place where the pressure is higher towards one where it is lower.[62]

In the paper (1715) already mentioned, Leibnitz says that 'a very strong wind can also support the weight of the air', [63] and goes on to explain that the winds can produce other effects, notably those of the opposing contrary winds referred to at the beginning of this section.

But the man who made the most determined attempt to explain the movements of the mercury by the effects of wind was De Mairan in his prize essay of 1715,[64] where he goes to great lengths to show that any moving body, including the air, presses less heavily on the surface beneath it than the same body at rest. It is fairly clear from his paper that De Mairan was mainly reflecting the ancient folk myth, derived from such elementary observations as the possibility of running quickly over thin ice. In fact he even cites Homer as describing the speed of a chariot by saying that its wheels left only the slightest tracks in the finest dust. Nevertheless it would be of great interest to know whether he had vaguely in mind the comparatively recent demonstration of centrifugal force by Christian Huygens.[65] Deluc assumed that De Mairan was thinking of centrifugal force, and showed that a violent gale of about sixty miles an hour would change the height of the barometer by only 1/244 of a line.[66] It is of some topical interest to note that Huygens calculated the speed at which a projectile would have to move in order to go into orbit. At any rate Deluc quite demolished De Mairan's theory, and it is absolutely astonishing that in the nineteenth century John Leslie should have contributed a long article to the *Encyclopaedia Britannica* in which he developed at some length a theory of his own

[61] There is a long paragraph about him in A. Wolf, *A History of science, technology, & philosophy in the 18th Century*, 2nd ed., 2 vol., London & New York, 1952. Paperback edition, New York, Harper 1961; Vol. I, pp. 274–5.

[62] C. von Wolff, *Aerometriae elementa, in quibus aliquot aeris vires ac proprietates juxta methodum geometrarum demonstrantur*. 2nd ed., Leipzig 1709, pp. 303 ff. (*Ed. princ.* 1702).

[63] Leibnitz, *Ephem. Acad. Nat. Cur.*, Cent. III & IV, appendix, pp. 50–51.

[64] Note 51, this chapter.

[65] Huygens, *Horologium oscillatorium*. Paris, 1673.

[66] Deluc, *Modifications*, ¶ 195. A line is 1/12 of an inch.

in which he treated winds as trying to blow off the earth at a tangent.[67] Somehow he managed to persuade himself that the farther a wind blows in more-or-less the same direction, the greater the diminution of atmospheric pressure beneath it, and he gave calculations purporting to show the magnitude of the effect. Leslie's reputation as a scientist was very great, but alas, this was not the last time that the innocent purchasers of encyclopaedias were to have their confidence betrayed by a famous man with a bee in his bonnet.

5. THE ADVECTION OF AIR

One of the prejudices that had to be overcome before meteorology could make real progress was the belief that the atmosphere, like the ocean, had a definite upper boundary, more-or-less equidistant from sea-level over the entire globe. To see how far we have come from this simple model one has only to think of the contour maps at constant pressure for the upper air that are now in daily use by the forecasters.

The clearest early statement that the 'height of the atmosphere' might vary seems to have been made by Philippe de la Hire, who looked after the weather observations at the Paris Observatory in the early years of the eighteenth century. In 1705[68] La Hire speculated that the large variations in the barometer must correspond to variations in the total height of the atmosphere, 'for it seems unreasonable to me to suppose, as some philosophers do, different fluids of different weights on the surface of the earth, sometimes carried one way and sometimes another; for these would usually have to be lighter when the air is more loaded with vapours, as observations show us'.[69] This, of course, was a bad reason for a good conclusion. He further conjectures that the atmosphere is a prolate spheroid with its axis coinciding with that of the earth. So, as it generally rains when the wind is southerly, the reason that the barometer falls in rainy weather is that the southerly winds are bringing overhead a portion of the

[67] *Supplement to the 4th 5th, and 6th Editions of the Encyclopaedia Britannica.* Edinburgh, 1824, Vol. 5, p. 329.
[68] La Hire, *Mém. Acad. Roy. Sci. Paris* (1705), 1–5.   [69] *Ibid.*, p. 3.

atmosphere that is not as deep. But on the other hand, if the wind is south only near the surface, and there is a north wind above, it can rain even though the barometer is rising.

Only a little later it began to be realized that temperature had a considerable effect on the density of the atmosphere. The researches of Guillaume Amontons on thermometry[70] probably drew attention to this; in any event, Placentini[71] thought it to be the chief cause of the variations of the barometer, arguing that as the height of the column of air remains constant, because it is a fluid, the pressure must be a function of the temperature. Notice that this is precisely the opposite of la Hire's argument, but it still presupposes advection at upper levels in order to restore the atmosphere to a uniform depth.

De Mairan[72] uses a similar argument to explain the high barometer in cold weather, and (he says) in cold countries. The cold causes the mass of air over the cold part of the earth to contract; but because fluids find their level, air from neighbouring parts will flow in at the top of the atmosphere, and there will then be more matter overhead, with the rise of pressure as a consequence. Similar ideas are expressed in the book by Christian Wolff already referred to,[73] and in a refreshingly undogmatic way, as befits a great philosopher. 'It is a great mistake in explaining Nature,' he writes, 'to ascribe to a single cause things that can have more than one.'[74] He makes the suggestion that the interruption of solar radiation by the clouds may warm them and the air above them, which may then move away 'to the side'.

Advection had to be introduced by Deluc[75] to explain how the addition of water vapour to the air could lower the barometer. The vapour tries to ascend because it is lighter, but as equilibrium is never attained, the whole air column always includes some of this specifically lighter material. It is objected that the added vapour will increase the mass of the column of air, and cause the barometer to rise; but, says Deluc, this column will spill over at the top on to the adjacent air where less evaporation has occurred, and as the specific

[70] Amontons, *Mém. Acad. Roy. Sci. Paris* (1702), 155–74.
[71] See note 50 in this chapter.   [72] See note 51.   [73] See note 60.
[74] *Ibid.*, Vol. II, p. 101.   [75] *Modifications*, ¶ 711–14.

gravity of the column is less, it will press less strongly on the mercury.

This was all very well in a qualitative way, but it could not be the sole cause, or even the main cause, of barometric variations. This was pointed out in 1783 by Horace Benedict de Saussure, about whom a few words seem desirable. He was born in 1740 at Geneva, where he became a Professor of Philosophy at the age of 22. At first attracted to botany, he soon devoted himself to the geology and meteorology of the Alps, which came to occupy his entire attention. He was the first great scientific mountaineer, and the observations that he found it necessary to make led him to invent numerous instruments and develop others. The most notable example is the hair hygrometer, the construction and calibration of which he described in his *Essais sur l'hygrométrie*,[76] a little masterpiece of experimental physics which also contains many of his ideas on rain. His greatest book, however, was the account of some (not all) of his scientific researches in the mountains.[77] There is little doubt that this strenuous life led to his death at the age of fifty-nine, after eight years of indifferent health. He was a paradigm of the distinterested scientific worker.

In his *Essais sur l'hygrométrie*, De Saussure says that Deluc's explanation of the cause of barometric variations seemed so plausible that he at first hoped that it could be confirmed by an *experimentum crucis*, and this was the reason for his researches with a large glass globe in which he found that the abstraction of all or nearly all the water vapour from air saturated at 16° R. lowered the pressure by only 1/54.[78] Thus even if we could suppose the whole atmosphere to pass from complete saturation to absolute dryness (which of course it would not), a change of only ½ [Paris] inch would result.

By considering various phenomena, especially the relatively small barometric changes near the equator, he shows that changes of temperature in restricted regions must be a greater cause of the

[76] Neuchâtel, 1783.

[77] *Voyages dans les Alpes, précédés d'un essai sur l'histoire naturelle des environs de Genève*. Neuchâtel, 1779–96, 4 vols. 4°. There was also an octavo edition in 8 volumes, 1780–96.

[78] Saussure, *Essais*, p. 283. The modern result is about 1/44.

84

variations of the barometer; these changes are partly brought about by the transfer of air from one place to another. To the objection that if cold causes the barometer to rise, it ought also to condense vapours and produce rain, De Saussure replies that in Europe the cold northerly winds are also the driest. They push away the air that was overhead before they came, and we have a high barometer with fine weather.[79]

De Saussure obviously was less of a system-builder than most of his contemporaries, and his modesty was equally untypical. In the course of the argument we are discussing he says:

> Without pretending to give a complete solution to such a difficult problem, one which such great physicists have in vain tried to solve, I shall content myself with proposing some general views.[80]

John Dalton had much the same ideas as De Saussure regarding the necessity of considering the variations of both temperature and moisture. He adduces an example that will be painfully clear to North American meteorologists:

> The climate of the eastern coast of North America is so constituted, that the decrease of the mean temperature in the winter season, in proceeding northward, is much more rapid than on the western coast of this continent [Europe]; the consequence is, that any particular place there is liable to great and sudden fluctuations of temperature in that season, and these produce proportionate fluctuations of the barometer, according as the warm and vapoury, or the cold and dry air predominate.[81]

Even if you did not know that water-vapour is lighter than air, you could explain how the barometer falls when moist air arrives from the south. Du Carla did this in 1780, on the theory that the moist air was relatively shallow, and communicated its heat to the air above, which dilated, and presumably flowed away at the top, though he did not make this clear.[82]

[79] *Ibid.*, pp. 304–5.   [80] *Ibid.*, p. 289.

[81] Dalton, *Meteorological observations and essays*, 2nd ed., Manchester and London, 1834; p. 104. (This was reprinted verbatim from the first edition, 1793).

[82] Marcellin Du Carla-Bonifas, *Les météores locaux*. Geneva 1780, p. 78. (This is the 7th *cahier* of this *Histoire naturelle du monde*.)

In 1788 Richard Kirwan published an 'Essay on the variation of the barometer',[83] in which he made a considerable forward step in attempting to show by calculation the inadequacy of many of the existing theories. For example, he showed that the changes in temperature in the first 5,000 feet of air, assumed not to depend on height, are not nearly sufficient to explain the changes of pressure across what we should now call a cold front; and he demonstrated numerically that the latter cannot merely result from the condensation of vapour. Then

> Having thus shown the insufficiency of those causes to which the variable weight of the atmosphere and height of the barometer have been usually referred, I now proceed to explain that which alone seems to me adequate to the effects produced; namely, the accumulation of air over those parts of the globe in which the mercury exceeds its mean height, that is the height suited to its situation, and the diminution or subtraction of the natural quantity of air over those regions in which the mercury falls beneath its mean height.[84]

Now the mean pressure is not very different in different parts of the earth, and therefore, since it is much warmer near the earth in the tropics, the atmosphere must be higher over the equator than over the poles. This was a very sound guess, as we now know, especially if we substitute 'tropopause' for 'atmosphere'. Also, says Kirwan, a relatively greater part of the mass of the atmosphere is found above a given medium level near the equator.

After this promising start Kirwan was diverted into the fashionable fields of chemical and electrical meteorology. He thought, for instance, that the upper atmosphere is chiefly 'inflammable air' (hydrogen), and that this is generated in great plenty between the tropics, flows north and south, and is burned up in the *aurora borealis* and *australis*; and that 'its combustion is the primary source of the greatest perturbations of the atmosphere'.[85]

It is more important that it was slowly coming to be realized that the variations of the barometer cannot be understood apart from the general circulation of the atmosphere. This was fully recognized,

[83] Kirwan, *Trans. Irish Acad.* 2 (1788), 43–72.
[84] *Ibid.*, p. 60.   [85] *Ibid.*, p. 62.

for example, by John Frederic Daniell, though his arguments, conducted by numerical example, are hard to understand.[86] He was aware of the importance of the distribution of land and water over the globe.

6. MISCELLANEOUS EXPLANATIONS

The difficulty of the barometer puzzle can be gauged by the intemperate flights of fancy that it engendered in really first-rate minds. One of these was Daniel Bernouilli, whose statement of the kinetic theory of gases was mentioned briefly in Chapter Two. The famous tenth section of his *Hydrodynamica*[87] is entitled 'On the constitution and motions of elastic fluids, especially air.' The first paragraphs of this, which contain the statement of the kinetic theory of gases (alas, so long before its time!), are often quoted. But there is a good deal more in this section, and for our purpose there is a demonstration that the height of the mercury in a barometer at a given altitude will be much more strongly affected by changes in the density of the air *below* it than in that of those above. There are large variations at the surface of the earth; therefore there must be air beneath its surface; and this is where Bernouilli plunges off at the deep end:

> . . . [it is] likely that for the most part, barometric variations are to be referred to rapid changes of heat in subterranean caves. It has long been known that there are many enormous caverns of this kind, and the pores in the solid earth may also act as caves. If you collect all the cavities (whether in the shape of caves or of pores containing air) down to a depth of 20,000 or 30,000 feet below the surface of the earth, and compare their capacity with the volume of the earth's crust down to the same depth, and put the latter at 1,000 or 100,000 times the former, yet certainly this cause will still be sufficient to explain the largest variations of the barometer . . .
>
> Some places near caves will be subject to larger changes of wind and of the barometer, because of the resistance of the air to motion. This is perhaps the reason why towards the equator, where there is ocean

[86] J. F. Daniell, *Meteorological essays and observations.* London, 1823.
[87] D. Bernouilli, *Hydrodynamica, sive de viribus & motibus fluidorum commentarii.* Strasbourg, 1738.

nearly everywhere, smaller variations of the barometer are observed than in these northern regions.[88]

The rapid subterranean changes may of course be manifested by earthquakes. Later in Section X, Bernouilli uses this idea to produce a really remarkable, but absurd, rule for barometric hypsometry; we need not consider this here.

Bernouilli's idea fortunately made almost no converts. A more extensive heresy was that in which the 'elasticity' of the air was thought to be independent of its 'weight', so that the reading of the barometer could be changed without the necessity of any change in the mass of the column of air overhead. As the believers in this doctrine seem – with the exception of one thoroughly denatured Englishman – to have been from the Continent, it is tempting to speculate that it may have arisen from the difficulty of understanding Robert Boyle, whose distinction between the 'spring' and 'weight' of the air may have obscured their intimate relationship for anyone whose native tongue was not English. Be this as it may, in 1701 we have Friedrich Hoffmann of Halle stating[89] that the height of the mercury depends 'not so much on the weight and mass of the air, but chiefly on the motion and expansive pressure of the aerial particles'.[90] This is greater when the air is dry, and in northerly winds, than when it is cloudy and rainy, and the wind southerly.

Everyone knew that many things in common use are stronger and springier when dry than when wet, so why not the atmosphere? This false analogy, which is probably at the basis of the doctrine we are considering, was succinctly expressed by Nikolaus von Beguelin:

> Experience teaches us that elastic bodies have a greater elasticity during dry weather, and that humidity weakens their spring. We are justified in concluding from this observation that the dryness of the air will

[88] *Ibid.*, pp. 211–12.

[89] Hoffmann, *Observationes barometrico-meteorologicae et epidemicae Halenses Anni MDCC, praemissae sunt curiosae physicae meditationes circa ventorum caussas* [etc.]. Halle, 1701.

[90] '*non tantum à pondere & mole aëris, sed maxime à motu & nisu expansivo particularum aëriarum.*' *Ibid.*, p. 57. I do not think we can regard this as a foreshadowing of the kinetic theory of gases, but the juxtaposition of *motus* and *nisus expansivus* is nevertheless very interesting.

increase the pressure of the atmosphere, and make it sustain a taller column of mercury.[91]

And the opposite for humidity. But because humid air is loaded with aqueous particles 800 times as dense as the air itself, it will weigh more, and dry air less. Therefore, concludes Beguelin, with a pyrrhonism appropriate to the Academy's meteorologist, there is no means of knowing *a priori* whether the pressure will rise or fall on account of humidity.

The doctrine without the doubts was expressed by Theodore Augustus Mann, an Englishman who at the time was Minister of Public Instruction at Brussels.[92] He appears to have believed it to be original. Passing over Joseph Stark,[93] for whom it was merely one of several possibilities, we shall only mention Jean Baptiste Van Mons, a Brussels professor of chemistry and physics, who came to the conclusion that the weight and pressure of the atmosphere change quite independently, and made simultaneous observations with a barometer and a 'manometer' to prove it.[94] The manometer was simply Boyle's 'statical baroscope', a light hollow ball hung on one arm of a balance;[95] It is a very insensitive instrument with a poor 'signal to noise ratio', as the electrical engineers would say, and it is not entirely surprising that Van Mons found what he was looking for. He concluded that it is a valuable addition to the meteorological armoury, and was astonished that De Saussure and others had 'confounded its indications with those of the barometer'.[96]

In another paper published the same year, Van Mons, who was an active member of the Belgian Academy, repeated even more emphatically his belief in the independence of the weight of the air and its elasticity.[97] He also revealed himself as one of the wildly speculative theorists who abounded at that period, as we shall see in Chapter VI. He writes about the interconversion of

[91] *Nouv. Mém. Acad. Berlin* (1774), 123.
[92] T. A. Mann, *Mém. Acad. Roy. Sci. Bruxelles.* 1 (1777), 263–84.
[93] *Bayerischen Akad., München, neue philos. Abh.* 4 (1785), 187–230.
[94] J. B. Van Mons, *Giornale di fisica, Pavia* 2 (1809), 317–23.
[95] See W. E. K. Middleton, *The history of the barometer*, p. 373.
[96] Van Mons, p. 323.
[97] J. B. Van Mons, *Nicholson's Journal* 24 (1809), 106–14.

light, the electric fluid, sublight, and subelectricity, if indeed this exist, and heat. We cannot take a single step in natural philosophy or chemistry, without perceiving the facility with which these agents are metamorphosed one into the other; a metamorphosis on which depends a very great number of phenomena.[98]

If, indeed, it exist.

One more theory should be considered; that which insists that in order that the barometer should fall or rise, part of the atmosphere must be absorbed or released. This idea was supported by P. N. Changeux of Paris, who designed an excellent early barograph and other instruments. Changeux thought the absorption and restitution or regeneration of air must be performed mainly by water, or by cloud.[99] When water evaporates, it disengages much air. This happens during fine weather, and the release of air is reflected in the rise of the barometer. When condensation begins, the water takes back its air and the barometer falls. This theory has a general resemblance to that of Lorenzo Pignotti, a professor of physics at Pisa who, influenced by Priestley's observations on combustion and respiration, and Cavendish's on the specific gravity of various gases, thought that 'phlogistic' vapours coming from the earth before rain diminish the weight of the lower part of the atmosphere.[100] But he did not exclude other secondary causes of barometric variation.

In conclusion let us refer to the prejudices of the immortal Goethe, whose writings on meteorology offer superfluous proof of the difference between poetry and science – or perhaps of the superiority of poetry. Goethe had a peculiar sensitivity to weather phenomena, combined with an insensitivity to the scientific climate of his time. The barometer seems to have fascinated him, and he came to the conclusion that the changes in air pressure, depending on causes entirely outside the atmosphere, actually *caused* all other meteorological phenomena. Wasielewski[101] records a pencilled note: 'The height of the barometer conditions all other atmospheric actions and is conditioned by none of them.' Goethe neglected the energy

[98] *Ibid.*, p. 107.   [99] Changeux, *Obs. sur la Phys.* 4 (1774), 85–103.
[100] L. Pignotti, *Congetture meteorologiche.* Firenze 1780, pp. 120 ff.
[101] Waldemar von Wasielewski, *Goethes meteorologische Studien.* Leipzig, 1910, pp. 28–29.

received from the sun, and because the changes of temperature did not seem to be closely connected with the barometric pressure, he paid little attention to them. It is clear from his own words that he had no adequate idea of the nature of atmospheric pressure:

. . . we seek the cause of the barometric variations not outside the terrestrial ball, but within it; it is not cosmic, not atmospheric, but rather telluric. Until a new light rises on us we persist in this hypothesis and say: the earth alters its force of attraction and attracts the atmosphere [*Dunstkreis*] more or less. This has no weight, nor does it exert any pressure, but when it is attracted more strongly it seems to press and weigh more heavily . . .[102]

But it is probably a good thing for us all that he was not a better scientist, for as H. von Ficker observed, 'with the busy, restless nature of this man, any more intensive occupation with meteorology would have shortened the time he had for other kinds of work better suited to his talents.'[103]

[102] Goethe, *Die Schriften zur Naturwissenschaft*. Erste Abteilung: Texte, Band 8, bearb. v. Dorothea Kuhn. Weimar, Hermann Böhlaus Nachf., 1962, p. 322.

[103] H. von Ficker, 'Bemerkungen über Goethes *Versuch einer Witterungslehre.*' *Sitz.-Ber. Preuss. Akad. Wiss.*, phys.-math. Kl. 7 (1932), 47–52. See also Karl Schneider-Carius, 'Goethe und die Meteorologie'. *Berichte des Deutschen Wetterdienstes in der U.S. Zone*, Nr. 12, Bad Kissingen, 1950.

Chapter Five

SEVENTEENTH- AND EIGHTEENTH-CENTURY THEORIES OF RAIN AND SNOW

Canst thou lift up thy voice to the clouds, that abundance of waters may cover thee?

Job, XXXVIII, 34

1. INTRODUCTION

In the last three chapters I have tried to lay an adequate foundation for a brief discussion of most of the theories of rain that were formulated in the seventeenth and eighteenth centuries. The term 'theory of rain' must here be understood as an attempt to explain the transition between suspended vapour and falling raindrops or snowflakes, the latter under conditions in which it is natural for water to appear in solid form.

Obviously the problem has two parts: the formation of cloud particles from vapour and the growth of raindrops from cloud particles. Yet in the absence of any detailed knowledge of cloud physics – a subject that belongs to the last eighty years or so – there was a tendency to run the two processes into one and to think about how invisible vapour could be turned into rain, the clouds being an inevitable intermediate stage in the process. Only in a few papers was there much speculation about the physical growth of raindrops, and in the later part of the period this was often connected with the observation that a raingauge nearer the ground collects more rain than one higher up.

At the end of the eighteenth century there occurred an unprecedented development of chemistry, following closely on great advances in the understanding of the phenomena of static electricity. This sudden enlargement of the scientific horizon led to a great deal of extravagant meteorological speculation that deserves a special chapter to itself (Chapter six).

2. ELEMENTARY IDEAS OF EXPANSION AND COMPRESSION

In 1637 Descartes speculated on what could cause cloud droplets to coalesce into raindrops. For this to happen at all, there must be an abundance of vapour, and it must be cold, so that the agitation of the 'subtle matter'[1] shall not prevent it.

> And it is also necessary that a west wind, opposing itself to the ordinary course of the vapours,[2] should assemble them and condense them in the place where it ends;[3] or else that two or more other winds, coming from various directions, should press the droplets and accumulate them between them; or that one of the winds should drive them against a cloud already formed; or else that the vapours should assemble at the bottom of some cloud, as they come out of the earth.[4]

It is extraordinarily difficult to understand how Descartes could be able to imagine that a wind could drive vapours against an existing cloud without the cloud moving off at precisely the same rate. It is possible that he had observed some of the apparently stationary clouds that form in a strong wind in the lee of a mountain crest, although these do not usually produce any rain. Yet his well-known theoretical ideas about continuity are hard to find in the above passage.

The idea of clouds being compressed and the particles driven together comes forward from time to time almost throughout the period. Noting that it sometimes rains while the barometer is rising George Garden observes that this is almost always after a sudden change of wind direction; in our terms, after the passage of a cold front:

---

[1] See p. 21 above.

[2] Descartes thought that the normal wind must be east, but did not assign a cause to this.

[3] '*aux endroits où il se termine.*'

[4] Descartes, *Les météores*, in *Oeuvres*, ed. Ch. Adam and Paul Tannery, Vol. 6, Paris 1902, pp. 283–4.

. . . if the winds do suddenly change into another quarter these vapours, which were formerly scattered into small particles, and so did easily float, are suddenly driven together into little drops and so must needs fall down into rain . . .[5]

Desaguliers wanted another sort of sudden action:

No gentle descent of a cloud, but only an accelerated motion downwards, produces rain.[6]

The exceptions are (1) the shock from a flash of lightning, and (2) collision of the cloud with a hill. The latter is not thought of as involving ascent:

[A cloud] meeting with an high hill in its way, will be condensed and fall in drops; especially if, in the day-time, it be driven by the wind out of the sunshine, against the shaded side of the mountain.[7]

Desaguliers's ideas are repeated, along with almost everyone else's, in that scientific dustbin the *Essai de physique* of Musschenbroek.[8] Even in 1765, the Rev. Hugh Hamilton of Dublin adduced, as the process by which clouds turn into rain, the driving together of their particles by the force of the winds;[9] and by 1772, when he published his *Modifications*, J. A. Deluc was still under the spell of this idea, which he presented beside a marginal sub-title 'Cause of rain':

When, by the abundance of vapour, by the support of a chain of mountains, by the action of a contrary wind, or lastly by the resistance that the clouds themselves oppose to the winds that carry them,[10] these clouds happen to be compressed; when this occurs the droplets of water touch and unite; the igneous particles that serve them as a vehicle[11] also unite and escape, the more easily the rarer the air, or the mountains themselves absorb these; thus raindrops are formed and fall, because they are heavier than air.[12]

[5] Garden, *Phil. Trans.* 15 (1685), 995.
[6] Desaguliers, *Phil. Trans.*, 36 (1729), 9.   [7] *Ibid.*
[8] Leyden, 1739. See pp. 742 ff.   [9] Hamilton, *Phil. Trans.* 55 (1765), 163.
[10] In the previous paragraph he had just said that clouds have almost the same specific gravity as the air in which they float!
[11] See p. 37 above.
[12] J. A. Deluc, *Recherches sur les modifications de l'atmosphère*. Geneva, 1772, ¶ 724.

Apparently the 'igneous particles' in the air could also be absorbed by the rain itself and carried down into the earth; this is the explanation given of a very big cold front on 21 August 1764, when the temperature suddenly fell from 22°R. to 8°R. (27.5°C. to 10°C.).[13]

Deluc never quite abandoned the idea of the particles coming into contact, but in his later writing made less of the clouds being compressed. By 1786 he had decided that rain clouds differ from others in that *so much vapour is being formed* that the particles – vesicles by this time – come into contact and unite, finally breaking like large soap bubbles and leaving drops, which sweep up more vesicles on their way down.[14]

Another group of Natural Philosophers took the diametrically opposed view that the dilatation of the air, not its compression, is necessary if raindrops, or even clouds, are to be formed. This point of view is well expressed by Edmond Halley:

> . . . the air being heap'd up by the meeting of two contrary winds, when the mercury is high, the vapours are the better sustained and kept from coagulating or condensing into drops, whereby clouds are not so easily generated; and in the night the vapours fall down single as they arose in imperceptible atoms of water. Whereas when the mercury is low and the air rarified by the exhaustion thereof, by two contrary winds blowing from the place; the atoms of air keep the vapours not so well separated, and they coalese into visible drops in the clouds; and from thence are easily drawn into greater drops of rain.[15]

Pardies, who thought clouds were made of little bubbles, believed that raindrops are formed when these break, 'whether because the air that they contain is rarefied to an extraordinary degree, or for some other reason'.[16] It is not quite clear whether he means that the air outside them must be rarefied too.

Eighty years later Du Carla, who appears importantly farther on,

[13] *Ibid.*, ¶ 720 and note (a). By European standards, a tremendous fall.
[14] Deluc, *Idées sur la météorologie.* 2 vols., London, 1786, ¶ 621. The reader will find the phrase which I have italicised more meaningful when he has read Chapter VI.
[15] Halley, *Phil. Trans.* 17 (1693), 473.
[16] Pardies, *Mém. de Trevoux*, Mar.–Apr. 1701, p. 165.

based his excellent theories on the idea that it is the rarefaction of the air that leads to the condensation of water in an ascending current.[17]

The origin of this idea was undoubtedly the famous and universally admired 'cloud-chamber' experiment of Otto von Guericke,[18] which every physicist and indeed nearly every scientific amateur had seen performed. Here one could *see* cloud being formed by the rarefaction of moist air, and apparently by this alone, for until about 1755 it was not realized that the expansion also produced a fall in temperature.[19] It was also noticed that under the appropriate conditions a very slight rarefaction was sufficient.

3. 'SALINE EXHALATIONS'

Immediately after the passage quoted above by Halley, we find the following:

> To which 'tis possible and not improbable, that some sort of saline or angular particles of terrestrial vapour being immixt with the aqueous, which I take to be bubbles, may cut or break their skins or coats, and so contribute to their more speedy condensation into rain.[20]

He had previously speculated that if the whole earth were covered with deep water there would be no diversity of weather

> other than periodically, every year alike; the mixture of all terrestrious, saline, heterogeneous vapours being taken away: which as they are variously compounded and brought by the winds seem to be the causes of those various seasons which we now find.[21]

This is almost certainly a reference to, or inspired by, the 'nitro-aerial spirits' of Mayow, discussed in Chapter four. In 1715 Edward Barlow thought that the production of rain seems to need the addition of 'essences of minerals, and sulphurous exhalations, out of the bowels of the earth'.[22] Musschenbroek naturally mentioned them.

[17] Du Carla, *Des météores locaux*. Geneva, 1780.   [18] See p. 45 above.
[19] See T. S. Kuhn, *Isis* 44 (1958), 132–40; also p. 104 below.
[20] Halley, *Phil. Trans.* 17 (1693), 473. *Cf* pp. 73 and 75 above.
[21] *Ibid.*, p. 470.
[22] *Meteorological Essays* [etc.]. London, 1715, p. 44.

But, rather surprisingly, these substances do not seem to have figured very largely in the history of the theories of rain.

4. THE GROWTH OF RAINDROPS

In Chapter one we discussed the strange theory of Aristotle that the largest raindrops – and hailstones – come from nearest the ground. This was too much for the seventeenth century, and all the authors who discussed the subject, as far as my reading goes, agree that raindrops usually increase in size the farther they fall. Not very many writers seem to have been interested in the subject at all. Two obvious mechanisms for the growth of raindrops present themselves to the mind: the coalescence of drops as they descend, and the condensation of water on to the falling drops.

The second of these alternatives seemed to appeal to Antoine Le Grand, a cartesian philosopher living in Oxfordshire. In summer, he said, the raindrops are larger, because 'they fall from higher regions, and in traversing a longer path in the air, increase in size on the way, gathering water to themselves'.[23] Exactly the same opinion was expressed in 1686 by Edme Mariotte, with the additional note that the clouds are lower in winter.[24]

The other alternative appealed to Barlow, who ascribed the coalescence of the elements that form precipitation to their different rates of fall, the larger overtaking the former.[25] In one of his better passages, Musschenbroek ascribes the different rates of fall to different ratios of surface to volume, and also notes that raindrops quickly accelerate to the maximum speed corresponding to their size. He also gives a valid explanation of the maximum size of raindrops (about 6 mm): the resistance of the air tears them apart if they become any larger, the 'attractive virtue' being insufficient.[26]

Hamilton also adopted the coalescence theory of the growth of raindrops:

[23] Le Grand, *Antonii le Grand Historia naturae, variis experimentis et ratiociniis elucidata* [etc.]. 2nd ed., London, 1680, p. 273.

[24] E. Mariotte, *Traité du mouvement des eaux et des autres corps fluides*. Edition of 1718 (Paris), pp. 18–19. (Ed. princ. 1686).

[25] *Meteorological Essays*, p. 47.   [26] *Essai de physique*, pp. 794–5.

and, for this reason, the drops, which fall from the higher clouds in summer, are found to be generally larger than they are in winter, when the clouds are low.[27]

But shortly after this the question received a new impetus from some experiments with rain gauges, made in Westminster by the celebrated physician William Heberden the elder.[28] Three similar funnels were constructed; one was placed near the ground, one above the highest chimneys of a house, and the third on the roof of Westminster Abbey, in a position where it would not be sheltered by the western towers. In every month from July 1766 to June 1767 the apparent rainfall decreased as the height increased, the grand totals being 22.608 inches in the garden, 18.139 inches on the house, and only 12.099 inches on the roof of the Abbey.[29] Clearly such an enormous effect must have a cause; this, says Heberden, has not been discovered, but

> It is probable, that some hitherto unknown property of electricity is concerned in this phaenomenon. This power has undoubtedly a great share in the descent of rain, which hardly ever happens, if the air and electrical apparatus be sufficiently dry, without manifest signs of electricity in the air.[30]

Those who knew most about electricity were the most cautious in using it as an explanation. Benjamin Franklin, writing in 1771 to Dr Thomas Percival on the subject, could see that every raindrop 'receives continual addition in its progress downwards', and suggested two possible mechanisms: that by which a bottle filled with cold water attracts moisture 'from the seemingly dry air that surrounds it'; and that by which an electrified body attracts dust. Raindrops coming from above are cold, and are known to be electrified; but Franklin did not think that enough was known about the matter at the time for a sound theory to be put forth.[31]

[27] *Phil. Trans.* 55 (1765), 164.
[28] *Phil. Trans.* 59 (1769), 359–62. (Page 362 is mis-numbered 262).
[29] Data were almost never 'rounded off' in the eighteenth century.
[30] Heberden (1769), pp. 361–2.
[31] Franklin to Percival, from London in 1771, in *Memoirs of Thomas Percival, M.D.*, London, 1807. Appendix, p. ccxliv–ccxlvi.

The importance of the raingauge experiments was clear to Daines Barrington. When he heard of Heberden's experiments he had two gauges put up in north Wales, both near the ground but with a vertical difference of elevation of 1,350 feet. By an incredible piece of good – or bad – luck he found an insignificant difference in the readings.[32] A note by a somewhat chastened Heberden was appended to Barrington's paper, ending

> This difference therefore does not . . . depend on the greater quantity of atmosphere, through which the rain descends: though this has been supposed by some, who have thence concluded that this appearance might readily be solved by the accumulation of more drops, in a descent through a greater depth of atmosphere.[33]

We should probably not pay much attention to the phrase 'more drops' in this quotation. What it was then thought possible to decide by such experiments was whether drops grew by union with smaller drops or by the acquisition of more water from the moist atmosphere. We now know that both processes occur, and indeed one of the most complex problems of recent cloud physics has been to decide on their relative contribution. As to the problem of the raingauges at different heights, a solution appeared much later, as will be made clear in Chapter eight.

Benjamin Franklin comes into this part of our story once again. On 22 December 1784, he communicated a paper to the Manchester Literary and Philosophical Society entitled 'Meteorological Imaginations and Conjectures'. One of these may be quoted in full.

> It is possible that, in summer, much of what is rain, when it arrives at the surface of the earth, might have been snow, when it began its descent; but being thawed, in passing through the warm air near the surface, it is changed from snow to rain.[34]

In this belief he was anticipated by J. H. Lambert, who deduced it from the fact that rain is often colder than the air at the ground.[35] Nowadays it is believed that a great deal of rain begins its fall as snow.

[32] *Phil. Trans.* 61 (1771), 294–7.   [33] *Ibid.*, p. 297.
[34] Franklin, *Mem. Manchester Lit. & Phil. Soc.* 2 (1789), 374.
[35] Lambert, *Abh. Akad. München*, II Theil, 3 (1765), 150.

5. THE EFFECT OF THE TERRAIN

It must have been a common observation on westward or south-ward-facing coasts that more rain falls in the hills inland than in the flat country near the seashore. The modern name for precipitation induced by the presence of the hills is *orographic precipitation*, and we now know that the cause of the greater rainfall in the mountains is that the air is cooled by its forced ascent in flowing over them. But long before this was understood, Halley wrote a magnificent account of the hydrological cycle, in which he first supposes an earth covered entirely by the ocean;[36] but it has, in fact, high mountains,

> which far surpass the usual height to which the aqueous vapours of themselves ascend, and on the tops of which the air is so cold and rarified as to retain but a small part of those vapours as shall be brought thither by the winds.[37]

So water is precipitated,

> gleeting[38] down by the crannies of the stone; and part of the vapour entring into the caverns of the hills, the water thereof gathers as in an alembick into the basons of stone it finds . . . This, if we may allow final causes, seems to be the design of the hills, that their ridges being placed through the midst of the continents, might serve as it were for alembicks to distil fresh water for the use of man and beast, and their heights to give a descent to those streams to run gently, like so many veins of the macrocosm, to be the more beneficial to the creation.[39]

Before about 1780, the only other writers to emphasize the role of the hills seem to have been Desaguliers (1729)[40] and Musschen-broek, though Deluc (1772) had used them as one way of 'compress-ing' clouds.[41] Deluc made many observations in the mountains, but the original reason for them was the improvement of barometric hypsometry, and this undoubtedly rendered him somewhat selective in his consideration of his results. He also made two separate bad decisions in the construction of hygrometers,[42] and these had an

---

[36] See p. 95 above.   [37] Edmond Halley, *Phil. Trans.* 17 (1693), 470.
[38] 'gleet: to ooze, flow slowly (obsolete).' O.E.D.
[39] *Phil. Trans.* 17 (1693), 470, 473.   [40] See p. 94 above.   [41] See p. 94.
[42] See W. E. K. Middleton, *Quart. J. Roy. Meteorol. Soc.* 68 (1942), 247–61.

influence on his ideas about rain. We shall come back to him in Chapter six.

But the most emphatic statement of the effect of the terrain was made by Du Carla in the book already referred to in Chapter three,[43] and in later papers.[44] He adduces dozens of examples of winds that deposit their moisture on the windward sides of mountains, the most imposing example being in the South American cordillera, high enough to remove every bit of moisture from the easterly wind, which is like a dry sponge when it gets to Peru, and dries everything up in its effort to regain its moisture. In his 1781 paper Du Carla brings the idea home by supposing a wall several thousand fathoms high on the meridian of the Observatory of Paris, and a constant east wind blowing. This, he says,

> would give to Vincennes a perpetual deluge, and make Marly an absolute desert, although Vincennes and Marly are not six leagues apart.[45]

If the wind were from the west, their climates would be reversed. A wall – or a mountain range – of lesser height would only partly dry the air passing over it, but even a very slight elevation will precipitate some of the moisture from saturated air. In general, wet winds are those that are ascending, dry winds those that are coming down.

Du Carla's book, which surely cannot have been printed in a very large edition, attracted less attention than it deserved. Besides emphasizing the importance of mountains in the production of rain, he was clear about the cause of the 'stationary' clouds in the lee of mountains, and he was also the first, as far as I know, to realize that air can be lifted by denser air running beneath it, although he applied this idea only to central Africa. The passage in question is as follows:

> The sun, which has passed into the northern hemisphere, is over the Mountains of the Moon at the beginning of April. This is where the 'eyes' of the Nile are: the air that covers them, more rarefied at that

[43] Marcellin Ducarla-Bonifas, *Histoire naturelle du monde, Septième cahier,* Geneva 1780. Paged separately, this part is entitled *Les météores locaux.*
[44] *Obs. sur la Phys.* 18 (1781), 446–66; *Ibid.* 19 (1782), 58–79.
[45] *Obs. sur la Phys.* 18 (1781), 447.

time than all the rest of the air in the same meridian, is raised by the
air from the north, which, coming from the region of winter, is the
most condensed . . .[46]

6. CONVECTION

We have already noted that Du Carla, probably independently
of Franklin and Lambert, had observed that unequal heating of
various parts of the terrain produces convection.[47] Whenever the
surface of the mountains is warmer than the air, rising currents are
produced, leading to condensation and eventually to rain. But it is
noteworthy that Du Carla thinks that the internal heat of the earth
is responsible for making mountain summits almost constantly
warmer than the air surrounding them;[48] in fact he seems to think
that they maintain an almost constant temperature of 10°R. at all
seasons.

De Saussure, who had read Du Carla, developed an elaborate
theory of the rise of vapour by convection.[49] He first assumes a
perfectly dry atmosphere over a moist terrain warmed by the sun.
The air, warmed, ascends, and is 'continually replaced by a north
wind'. It appears that he is thinking of Geneva, where a wind called
the *sechard* (the 'drying wind') rises at about 08h or 09h in settled
fine weather.

If instead the air is already saturated, some cloud particles –
'vesicles' of course – will be formed near the ground, but will again
be dissolved by the slightly warmed air; this will be carried up by
the vertical current until it is at a level where clouds can again form.
The thickness of the clouds will increase as long as the supply of
vapour goes on, but they will finally cut off the sun's light and heat
from the lower layers and either the clouds will descend or it will
rain.

De Saussure frequently writes of a *column* of air, adjacent columns,
and so forth, and it seems likely that he had at least a vague idea of
what are now called convection cells. In a note on p. 277 of the

[46] *Les météores locaux*, p. 27.   [47] See p. 61 above.
[48] *Les météores locaux*, pp. 37–42.   [49] *Essais sur l'hygrométrie*, pp. 261 ff.

Essais he observes that ascending air must be replaced by winds blowing in from cooler regions. But he did not make himself at all clear about this, and certainly not to Deluc, who in 1787 strenuously denied the existence of ascending currents of air.[50] One of his arguments is that if warm air rose because of the heat it receives from the sun, it would not be colder at the tops of the mountains, though as we shall see in a moment, this argument had been refuted by J. H. Lambert. But some of his objections are so stupid that it is impossible not to believe that they were motivated by nothing more than the desire to demolish the idea of vertical convection at any cost, for it was damaging to Deluc's peculiar theory of rain which will be considered in the next chapter. For example:

> Mr. De Saussure goes on speaking of a *column*; but all the causes in question are common to a very large portion of the hemisphere illuminated by the sun's rays.[51]

I am unwilling to believe that an experienced mountaineer like Deluc would not realize that the air over sloping ground facing south would be warmed much more than that over a northward-facing slope; at least after his attention had been drawn to it. He could not have been expected to know, as we know, that different surfaces reflect and consequently absorb heat to various degrees; but surely he could have noticed the difference between rocks and snow.[52]

At the same period Andrew Oliver of Salem, Massachusetts, was using the concept of convection to explain waterspouts,[53] and no better explanation of these striking phenomena appeared for many years after.

7. COOLING BY RAREFACTION

Du Carla clearly thought that it is the rarefaction of the rising air that leads to the condensation of some of the water in it, and even stated that the amount precipitated per unit area in unit time is proportional

---

[50] Deluc, *Idées sur la météorologie*, 2 vols., London, 1786, ¶ 600 and ¶ 651.
[51] *Ibid.*, ¶ 661.   [52] See also p. 83 above.
[53] Oliver, *Trans. Amer. Philos. Soc.* 2 (1786), 101–17.

to the rate of ascent.[54] But did he know that there is a necessary connection between rarefaction and cooling? Apparently he did, for in 1781 he states clearly that

> The air . . . cannot rise in the atmosphere without becoming colder and more rare, and without losing, *on both counts*, its property of holding heterogeneous substances in solution.[55]

The phrase that I have italicized makes it clear that his knowledge of the process was quite empirical, and that he still believed that rarefaction alone was capable of causing the condensation of water vapour. This had been common doctrine ever since Guericke's 'cloud chamber' experiment.

In 1755 William Cullen, then professor of medicine at Glasgow, noted the cooling of air that was quickly expanded in the laboratory, but ascribed it to evaporation of water incidentally contained in the apparatus.[56] No theoretical progress was made until J. H. Lambert published his *Pyrometrie* in 1779, where he explained the phenomenon, and also the heating of air by compression, in terms of changes in the concentration of the particles of 'fire', *i.e.* of the elastic fluid of which heat was supposed to consist.[57] It is easy to see how logical an explanation this seemed to provide. But Lambert did more. He gave a theoretical explanation, depending on the relative lightness of 'fire', for the decrease of temperature with increasing altitude. After noting that heat rises in air, he continues:

> Such an upward motion of heat goes on in the air all the time. For the heat which the earth receives from the sun throughout the year goes up into the air, so that the earth continues to need new heat from the sun if it is not to get colder and colder. Inasmuch as the upward motion of the heat depends on its smaller weight, its velocity will go on increasing as it ascends. This has the result that the particles of fire, which follow each-other in their upward motion, get farther and farther apart—the sort of thing one sees if a falling sphere is observed every tenth of a second. The distances between them will increase

[54] *Les météores locaux*, p. 29.   [55] *Obs. sur la Phys.* 18 (1781), 448. Italics added.
[56] William Cullen, *Edinb. Phil. Soc. Essays Phys. & Lit.* 2 (1755), 159–71. See also T. S. Kuhn, *Isis* 44 (1958), 132–40.
[57] Lambert, *Pyrometrie oder vom Maase des Feuers und der Wärme.* Berlin, 1779, p. 266–71.

according to the numbers 1, 3, 5, 7, etc. For this reason, the density of the particles of fire is less in the upper air, and thus it is colder.[58]

This superlatively clear explanation seems not to have been noticed by the meteorologists.

At any rate, the subject was tackled afresh by that extraordinary man Erasmus Darwin, the grandfather of Charles Darwin, who has been greatly under-rated because he wrote poetry of a kind that soon became unfashionable, and held political views that became more unfashionable still.[59] But he was a man of many parts, and our special interest in him concerns a paper that he wrote in 1788.[60] Its title sets forth the programme:

Frigorific experiments on the mechanical expansion of air, explaining the cause of the great degree of cold on the summits of high mountains, the sudden condensation of aerial vapour, and of the perpetual mutability of atmospheric heat.

The 'frigorific experiments' are four in number:
(1) When the air from 'the receiver of an air-gun' is played on the bulb of a thermometer, the mercury descends;
(2) It also descends when the thermometer is in a vessel that is being exhausted by an air pump;
(3) It descends when the bulb is exposed to a stream of air from 'the air vessel of a water-works', i.e. the vessel which, besides collecting air, smooths out the pulsations produced by a reciprocating pump;
(4) An observation reported by [K.F.?] Wolff in 1761, in which snow and ice collected at the outlet of a 'Hero's fountain' in Hungary, with a head of 260 feet.[61] From all these, says Darwin,

there is good reason to conclude, that in all circumstances, when air is mechanically expanded, it becomes capable of attracting the fluid matter of heat from other bodies in contact with it.[62]

[58] Ibid., p. 232.
[59] A spirited attempt to rehabilitate him has recently been made by Desmond King-Hele, Erasmus Darwin, London, 1963. Mr King-Hele, a mathematical physicist with a flair for literary criticism, is one of the few twentieth-century men as versatile as Erasmus Darwin.   [60] Darwin, Phil. Trans., 78 (1788), 43–52.
[61] Wolfe [Wolff], Phil. Trans. 52, Part 2 (1762), 547–54. Wolff ascribes the freezing to the 'saline, nitrous, and sulphurous water' in the mine.
[62] Phil. Trans. 78 (1788), 47.

and he correctly applies this phenomenon to explain the coldness on mountains and in the upper air, which was then beginning to be verified by balloonists. He also coined a word, *devaporation*, synonymous with the condensation of vapour, but really a better word, for 'condensation' can also mean something else, both in etymology and in usage. But the O.E.D., which quotes Darwin for this word, found no takers, which is a pity.

In this paper he also notes that in 'aerial devaporation',

> a quantity of heat is set at liberty along with the excess of devaporation [*i.e.* the condensate], and the atmosphere becomes warmer than before the beginning condensation,[63]

but this was of course Joseph Black's discovery of latent heat, which had not been published formally by Black, but was well known to the group of people in and near Birmingham to which Erasmus Darwin belonged,[64] as well as James Watt and Joseph Priestley.

John Dalton in 1793 was content to interpret the heating of air by compression as being a result of the precipitation of a portion of its vapour, which gives up its latent heat to the air. He had apparently not changed his opinion by 1834,[65] and indeed the part played in the phenomena of the weather by the latent heat of condensation only began to be understood in the 1830's.

We seem to have come rather a long way from the actual theory of rain, but the pertinence of these considerations will appear when we come to deal with nineteenth-century developments in Chapter Eight.

8. HUTTON'S THEORY OF RAIN

In the year of Erasmus Darwin's paper there was published a theory of rain, read to the Royal Society of Edinburgh in 1784 by the celebrated Scottish geologist James Hutton whose *Theory of the earth* is a milestone in that subject. In his paper, entitled 'The theory of Rain',[66] Hutton began by considering why the breath is visible in cold

[63] *Ibid.*, p. 51.
[64] See Robert E. Schofield, *The Lunar Society of Birmingham*, Oxford, 1963, *passim*.
[65] Dalton, *Meteorological observations and essays*, 2nd ed., pp. 190–1.
[66] *Trans. Roy. Soc. Edinb.* 1 (1788), 41–86.

weather. This cannot be explained, he says, by 'the general principles of heat and cold', but must depend on the 'dissolving power' of air varying non-uniformly with temperature. It is known that warmer air will 'dissolve' more water; but what is the precise relation between temperature and 'dissolving power'? This may have one of three forms (fig. 5.1): the straight line *mr*, some curve *mkr* concave down-

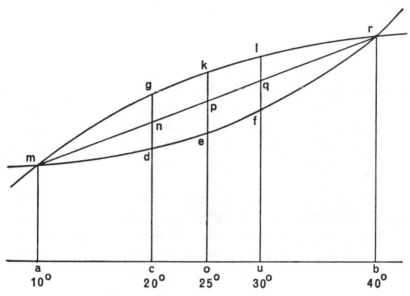

FIG. 5.1. To illustrate Hutton's theory of rain

wards, or some curve *mer* concave upwards. Now if the ordinates *am* and *br* represent the quantities of water that saturate a given volume of air, at the temperatures *a* and *b*, then the quantities of water, 'dissolved' [*i.e.* in the form of vapour] or not, in all mixtures of saturated air at these two temperatures will be represented by the ordinates of *mr*.[67] Thus if the law were represented by the line *mr*, all mixtures of saturated air would be exactly saturated. If one or both components were less than saturated, no mixture could possibly be saturated.

[67] G. I. Taylor, *Q. J. Roy. Meteorol. Soc.* 43 (1917), 241–68, has objected that this is not axiomatic as Hutton supposed, and has given a proof of it.

But if the law is some curve such as *mer*, and any quantities oi saturated air at the temperatures *a* and *b* be mixed, then *op*, for example, the quantity of water available, will be equal to the amount *oe* required to saturate the mixture, plus *ep*, which will appear as liquid water. If the curve were like *mkr* any such mixture would be unsaturated, since *ok* > *op*. The very fact that breath and steam become visible show that this cannot be the form of the curve, and that the 'dissolving power' of the air is in fact an increasing function of the temperature.

A visible condensation requires a sufficient degree of saturation in the two atmospheres that are to be mixed. 'It is sufficient, that the difference in the temperatures of those portions to be mixed should more than compensate the defect in point of saturation.'[68] Hutton could easily have shown this on the diagram, but he did not.

He believed that this mixing is the fundamental cause of rain and snow, and supported the idea by two observations of snow having resulted when very cold air is suddenly let into a warm room, an observation not at all uncommon in sub-arctic climates in winter. But this is far from all. He maintained that in the absence of condensation by mixing of the lower polar current and the upper equatorial one, we should have drought all summer and rain all winter. We have not the space to follow closely the thirty-odd quarto pages on 'the theory of rain applied to natural appearances' which constitute Part II of his paper.[69] It was a noble effort, but it suffered from one fatal defect: it was qualitative, and if he had been able to put numbers into it he would have seen how inadequate it was, even if the required mixing could have been shown to take place. The visibility of the breath in cold weather and the appearance of visible steam over a cauldron are excellently explained by his theory, but among meteorological phenomena only a limited class of fogs are really produced by the process that he invoked.

His theory was immediately attacked by J. A. Deluc, who would not even grant him the visible breath of animals or the steam from the kettle as a result of mixing,[70] let alone any rain. In this respect

---

[68] Hutton (1788), p. 47.   [69] *Ibid.*, pp. 52–86.
[70] Deluc, *Idées sur la météorologie*, ¶ 580–8.

Deluc's arguments are quite unconvincing. Hutton replied in a paper read to the Society in December 1787;[71] a very polite paper in the main, though near the end he permits himself to observe that

> . . . any person who has read [Deluc's] later publications, will hardly expect, that, with his meteorological ideas, our author should, on this occasion, be altogether free from partiality.[72]

We shall see in the next chapter how just this was. Although I have read Deluc's books and papers on this subject at intervals for twenty years, I have only recently realized that in the 1780s he was the victim of an obsession; he could not bear to have anyone else propose a theory of rain different to his own. As soon as he saw Hutton's reply he wrote him a long letter, dated 4 December 1789, and rushed it into print in the *Monthly Review*.[73] In this letter he repeats his previous objections, and then says that it is not the hypothesis of mixing that he is objecting to, but the theory of rain derived from t. Characteristically, he even claims that he thought of the hypothesis first. He then shows by a single numerical example the quantitative insufficiency of the theory, and this single paragraph justifies the letter. I have not found out what Hutton thought of this; but there is no doubt that Deluc was much the more able controversialist. At the end of the letter he replies to the charge of partiality with the astonishing claim that his new ideas have also caused him to abandon *his own* older theory, so that he cannot justly be accused of being partial!

Hutton's theory ought to have died an early death, but it lived on in the Encyclopaedias. John Leslie was still happy about it in 1824,[74] and in 1833 Luke Howard, in the second edition of his famous book on the London climate, felt that a job of demolition was in order. In rejecting the 'Huttonian theory of rain', he wrote:

> the safest course that we can follow, in reasoning on subjects connected with the operations of nature, is undoubtedly that of direct induction

[71] Hutton, *Trans. Roy. Soc. Edinb.* 2, Part II (1790), 39–58.
[72] *Ibid.*, p. 55.
[73] Deluc, *Monthly Review* 81 (1789), 695–707.
[74] In *Supplement to the 4th, 5th, & 6th Editions of the Encyclopaedia Britannica.* Edinburgh, 1824, vol. 5, pp. 359–60.

from observation and experiment: and in this we may be allowed to avail ourselves, not only of our own, but likewise of the published results of others. It sometimes happens, nevertheless, that the mere sally of an ingenious reasoner, especially if it be supported by an appearance of mathematical demonstration, shall obtain general acceptance on the credit of his name and previous labours, *without the least pretension to experimental proof or natural observation of any kind.* Such is, in fact, the so much praised Huttonian theory of rain.[75]

With this sententious pronouncement we may leave the subject.

[75] Luke Howard, *The Climate of London.* 2nd ed., 3 Vol., London, 1833; Vol. I, p. 124. The italics are Howard's.

Chapter Six

ELECTRICAL AND CHEMICAL METEOROLOGY

Meteorological phenomena . . . are manifestly due to immense chemical operations, and only chemistry can unveil their cause and penetrate their mysteries.

Fourcroy, SYSTÈME DES CONNAISSANCES CHYMIQUES. Paris, 1800, Vol. I, p. 7.

1. INTRODUCTION

The eighteenth century saw two series of events that were very unsettling to those seriously interested in meteorology. The earlier, which took place mainly between 1730 and 1760, was an immense expansion of knowledge about static electricity.[1] The later, which occupied the last thirty years of the century and continued into the nineteenth, is what is usually referred to as 'the chemical revolution', although it is felt by many people that this is an inappropriate term for a change which, however far-reaching, took so long to come about. But there is no doubt at all that chemistry was tremendously changed during this period.[2]

The influence of the new knowledge of electricity on meteorology was in reality not very great, and will first be treated briefly. The 'chemical' episode in the history of the hydrometeors is more interesting and complex. It will form the main subject of this chapter.

2. ELECTRICAL THEORIES

It is notable that the most dogmatic statements about the effects of the 'electric fire' on the weather were made by enthusiastic people

[1] For a concise account see Edmund Whittaker, *A history of the theories of aether and electricity*, Revised Ed., London, 1951, Vol. I, Chap. 2.

[2] See, for example, J. R. Partington, *A Short History of Chemistry*, 3rd ed., London, 1957, Chapters V to IX.

who had received their knowledge of electricity at second hand. With the possible exception of Beccaria, the great electrical experimenters of the eighteenth century – men such as Franklin, Watson, and Nollet – were more cautious in their meteorological speculations. As soon as the electrical nature of lightning was discovered the subject of atmospheric electricity grew rapidly, and it was found almost at once that raindrops nearly always carry an electrical charge. However, the subject of atmospheric electricity is outside the range of this book, and we must confine ourselves to the supposed effects of electricity on the formation and fall of the hydrometeors.[3]

Benjamin Franklin was the first to propose a theory of rain in which electricity played a prominent part. This was contained in a letter written to John Mitchell, F.R.S., and dated 29 April 1749. The letter was read to the Society but not well received, and was published only in 1751.[4] In 1749, three years before the famous experiment with the kite, Franklin was already of the opinion that the electricity of the atmosphere was the same as that of the laboratory. The electric fire, he thought, would assist the 'common fire' in expanding air. A discharge of the electric fire would thus allow cloud particles to come closer together, so that some of them might touch and coalesce. There could be two mechanisms for the discharge of strongly charged clouds coming from the sea. They could be driven against mountains (which would also cool them), or in the absence of mountains a cloud from the sea could meet a land cloud with much less charge, and be discharged by a lightning flash.

From his later rather tentative papers on this subject one may conjecture that Franklin would not have maintained this theory with any vigour.

The next to produce an electrical theory of the suspension of vapours and the fall of rain seems to have been the Irishman Henry Eeles, who communicated it to Thomas Birch, then Secretary of the

---

[3] Except for hail, which will be dealt with in Chapter X.
[4] In Franklin, *Experiments and observations on electricity* [etc.], London, 1751. pp. 36–49. This letter has been analysed in I. B. Cohen, *Franklin and Newton* [etc.]. Philadelphia, Amer. Philos. Soc., 1956, (*Memoirs*, Vol. 43), pp. 481–4.

Royal Society.[5] Eeles had apparently made electrical experiments. He believed that vapours and exhalations rise because electric fire is added to them, rendering them lighter than air. If then they happen to 'approach within their repulsive powers' and coagulate, their total surface will be reduced and so their electrical fluid will be lost to other particles; they will therefore become heavier and start to fall, impinging on other particles on the way. It is difficult to see why the electrical fluid has to be brought into this last process at all, except to get rid of the electricity that was postulated in order to raise the vapours. All ascending vapours are electrified, he maintained; he had performed experiments to prove it. Birch wrote to say that the Royal Society would like to hear about these experiments, and in another letter Eeles described them.[6] He had made a huge electroscope by hanging two pieces of down by fine silk threads from the middle of a horizontal thread eight feet long. When these were charged, either with resinous or vitreous electricity, they were not discharged by smoke, steam from a kettle, breath, and all the 'vapours and exhalations' he could think of. This he interpreted to mean that the ascending vapours must be either 'electrics, or non-electrics electrified'. He determined that they were non-electrics (i.e., conductors) by letting them condense on the surface of sealing wax or glass, which at once became conducting and discharged the down.

All this was rather ingenious, but it was promptly shot down by the young Erasmus Darwin in one of his earliest scientific efforts.[7] Darwin pointed out that an insulated feather may even be touched lightly several times with the finger without losing all its electrification. He also maintained that the rise of vapours, the suspension of clouds, and the fall of rain could be explained without the introduction of electrical forces.

At about the same time the Italian physicist Giovanni Battista Beccaria was studying electricity both in the laboratory and in the atmosphere. He had noted that a stream of water falling from the end of a tube breaks up into small drops when the tube is electrically

[5] *Phil. Trans.* 49 (1755), 124–54.   [6] *Ibid.*, p. 151–4.
[7] Darwin, *Phil. Trans.* 50 (1757), 240–54.

charged, and also that raindrops are electrified. Out of these phenomena he built an electrical theory of rain.

> . . . rain begins to form at the moment when a certain uniform and
> continuous current of electric fire begins to flow between the clouds
> and the earth . . . I shall show how such a current is by itself best suited
> to produce all the various well-ordered phenomena.[8]

He goes on to suggest that the earth is one terminal, and the top of a
cloud the other; the motions of the 'current' of electricity between
these can disperse the cloud particles or concentrate them until they
touch and come down. He supports this argument by reference to
his observations of electroscopes before, during, and after rain.

Beccaria's mistake, shared by a great many much less able men,
was to see analogies in the atmosphere for electrical phenomena
produced artificially in the laboratory. It would be tedious and un-
rewarding to consider all these ideas in detail;[9] I shall conclude with
a reference to Richard Kirwan, a chemist of much distinction. Rain,
said Kirwan

> is the immediate result of the union of the particles which form clouds;
> and this union is the consequence of the subtraction of the electric
> atmospheres which keep them at a distance from each other; . . .[10]

He supported this idea with plenty of specious reasons; for
example, southerly winds (he said) are more highly electrified than
the soil of more northerly countries; hence the large amount of
vapour they contain is rapidly deprived of part of its electricity
and converted into clouds. Even orographic rain has to be
accounted for electrically.[11]

Perhaps there is some inner compulsion to find electrical causes
for precipitation. At any rate a work was published as late as 1929
by two very reputable meteorologists, suggesting the application of

---

[8] Beccaria, *Elettricismo atmosferico. Lettere di Giambattista Beccaria.* 2nd ed:, Bologna,
1758, p. 302.

[9] Some examples: F. C. Achard, *Mém. Acad. Berlin* (1780), 14-23; A. Eason, *Mem.
Manchester Lit. & Phil. Soc.* I (1782), 395–405; M. Hube, *Ueber die Ausdünstung, und
ihre Wirkung in der Atmosphäre.* Leipzig 1790.

[10] Kirwan, *Of the variations of the atmosphere.* Dublin, 1801, p. 220.

[11] *Ibid.,* pp 226–7.

the results of colloid science to the problem.[12] But it is not now believed that the electrical state of a cloud has much effect on the development of precipitation.

3. CHEMICAL METEOROLOGY

Chemistry was introduced into meteorology at the end of the seventeenth century by the important French chemist Nicholas Lémery, who wished to explain all the more violent phenomena of nature – earthquakes, hurricanes, lightning, and thunder – by the combination of iron and sulphur in the depths of the earth.[13] This fantasy was derived from an experiment with iron filings and wet sulphur, in which large amounts of heat were produced, and often flame. Sulphurous winds from this reaction, he said, produce hurricanes; and he advised people caught in a hurricane to lie prone and put their mouths to the earth, 'not only to avoid being blown away, but so that they may not breathe this hot and sulphurous wind, which would suffocate them'.[14] It may not be entirely superfluous to mention that Lémery was a convinced Cartesian.

Chemistry really began to influence the theory of rain after the discovery and identification of various kinds of 'airs' (gases), by Black, Cavendish, Priestley, Scheele, Lavoisier, and others; and in particular after it was discovered that ordinary air is not a simple or elementary substance, but a mixture (mainly) of two gases, now called oxygen and nitrogen; and that water is a compound of hydrogen and oxygen. All these advances were made between 1760 and 1790, particularly in the 1780s.[15] Air and water are the 'raw materials' of meteorology, and it is not at all surprising that the chemical discoveries about them should have affected the subject. That they did so to such an extent and so quickly was chiefly the work of Jean André Deluc.

Deluc had become a close friend of James Watt, the great im-

---

[12] A. Schmauss and A. Wigand, *Die Atmosphäre als Kolloid.* Hamburg, 1929.
[13] Lémery, *Mém. Acad. Roy. Sci. Paris* (1700), 101–10.
[14] *Ibid.*, p. 105.
[15] The reader is strongly urged to consult Partington's *Short History of Chemistry*.

prover of the steam engine, and had come to know the circle of scientific men in and near Birmingham known as the Lunar Society.[16] One of the members of this circle was Joseph Priestley, who in the 1770's identified at least nine of the common gases, and in 1781 noticed that water is formed when hydrogen ('inflammable air') is exploded with oxygen ('dephlogisticated air') or common air. It seems that Deluc took a dislike to Henry Cavendish, who in 1781 had shown the constant composition of air, and in 1783 Deluc persuaded Watt that Cavendish was plagiarizing one of Watt's theories.[17] Deluc never seems to have accepted the fact that air is a mixture of two gases, and by 1790 he had even come to the conclusion that the theory of the composition of water was unfounded.[18] It is hard to avoid the impression that his personal relationships had a good deal to do with his science.

Yet it would be wrong to dismiss him as a crank or a visionary. It must be remembered that by the time his *Idées sur la météorologie* came out in 1786, he had been experimenting with meteorological instruments and thinking about atmospheric processes for nearly forty years, with a remarkable singleness of mind. He had started as a young man to try to explain the weather – the complicated weather of the Swiss Alps – and even after he moved to England in 1773 his favourite examples continue to be drawn from the mountains, perhaps because it was essential for him to adduce whatever information was available about the upper air, little as this amounted to.

It must be recognized that in 1786 meteorological theories were extremely vague and unsatisfactory. There was really neither enough information nor the necessary fundamental physical theory for it to be otherwise. Deluc's real fault was a complete lack of the humility appropriate to a scientific man; a theory was needed, and a theory he would produce. What may have started as a hypothesis became an obsession, and as a result, all inconvenient discoveries by others were simply ignored or else violently attacked.

[16] See Robert E. Schofield, *The Lunar Society of Birmingham*, Oxford, 1963, especially Chapters X and XI.

[17] Partington, *A Short history*, p. 143. Partington calls Deluc 'mischievous'.

[18] Deluc, *Obs. sur la Phys.* 36 (1790), 375-6.

The *Idées sur la météorologie* itself is a formidable document, more than a thousand pages of extremely verbose and repetitive argument, not at all improved by being liberally peppered with italics on every page. A large part of the first volume consists of a disagreement with H. B. de Saussure about the merits of their respective hygrometers, which need not detain us here. This is followed by 459 pages on 'Vapours, considered as a class of expansible fluids'. The distinctive characteristic of expansible fluids, according to Deluc, is that they are formed of 'a substance purely ponderable and a deferent fluid'.[19] Vapours differ from 'aeriform fluids' in that in vapours these two components are feebly held together. Among the 'vapours' he deals at enormous length with two, specially important: 'fire' and 'electric fluid'. Fire is not an element, but is composed of light, which acts as the deferent fluid, and a purely ponderous substance, which he calls *matière du feu*. This latter substance deprives light of its property of producing brightness, but imparts that of producing heat. It appears much later that fire (not light) itself acts as a deferent fluid for all gases (*fluides aeriformes*).[20]

Similarly Deluc supposes that the 'electric fluid' is composed of a ponderable fluid and a deferent fluid, and devotes about 300 pages to an elaborate discussion of many experiments on static electricity from this point of view. Near the end of Volume I he makes a profession of faith:

So I conclude from all these reflections, that as long as great phenomena are still to be explained, especially in meteorology, we must not limit the number of distinct substances to those directly known to us, above all in the class of expansible fluids, whose great importance in meteorological phenomena we are only beginning to discover. The atmosphere is a chemical laboratory, as important as the bowels of the earth for the physical phenomena of our globe. Until by our understanding we have leapt over the barriers of our senses, attributing to effects that are really analogous, causes of the same kind, we shall see only the rough exterior of Nature, and even the commonest phenomena will be obscure to our eyes. This is what I am proposing to show by means of examples in the last part of this work.[21]

[19] *Idées*, ¶ 113.   [20] *Ibid.*, ¶ 261.   [21] *Idées*, ¶ 535.

Here we have a sort of chemical manifesto; if the known substances will not serve to explain the phenomena, well then, let us imagine substances that will. Deluc sometimes seems to lose sight of the difference between identifying gases, as Priestley had been doing, and imagining them.

But before considering the second volume of the *Idées* it must be strongly emphasized that there existed two ideas of capital importance to our subject, to one of which Deluc strenuously objected, while he made no use whatever of the other.

The first idea is that of vertical convection, discussed by Lambert and used by De Saussure and Du Carla.[22] As we have seen in Chapter five, in 1786 Deluc could not or would not believe in the existence of ascending currents; and it is sad to record that he can be convicted of insincerity out of his own writings, for in a description of an exciting mountain journey with his brother in 1770 he records that they were observing the clouds in the morning after a terribly stormy night. Of these clouds

> Some dissipated on approaching the rocks that limited our view. Others, coming one after another, rose vertically along these rocks, and went to join the clouds that were passing overhead. Doubtless these rocks, which had kept part of the heat that they had received from the sun during the day, were dilating the air in the neighbourhood and the clouds themselves, producing an upward current of air, as in our chimneys.[23]

This was before he had a theory of his own, to be defended at all costs.

The second idea is the necessary connexion between the ascent of air and its cooling, demonstrated by Lambert in 1779[24] in terms of the material theory of heat – terms which Deluc could appreciate. Of course there is no reason to conclude that Deluc ever read Lambert's *Pyrometrie*; comparatively few people seem to have done so. But it is nevertheless very interesting to wonder how much difference it would have made if he had. Certainly his full acceptance of these two ideas – convection and cooling by ascent – would have rendered

[22] See p. 102 above.   [23] Deluc, *Recherches sur les modifications de l'atmosphère*, ¶ 916.
[24] See p. 104 above.

Deluc's own theory unnecessary and incidentally advanced meteorology by half a century.

Almost at the beginning of the second volume of the *Idées* Deluc states the problem that is really the subject of the book: 'in what state was the water before the rain formed?'[25] He had been led to question the usual explanation (that it is in the form of vapour) by a chance observation in the mountains in 1770. when a metal ferrule fell off a stick. The dryness aloft, made evident by this occurrence, had been confirmed by observations with hygrometers, both by De Saussure and by himself. He refers in particular to an occasion on the Sixt mountains in 1772, in which his hygrometer showed very dry air even while heavy clouds were forming around his party, and again immediately after the end of the tremendous storm that followed. This occasion, he goes on,

> had remained deeply engraved in my memory, especially because it threw my mind into the greatest confusion concerning everything about meteorology. Although I differed from the received opinion about the cause of evaporation, I had not doubted until then that rain was the direct inverse of it. But where was this water, where were all the ingredients of the tempest while my hygrometer showed such dryness even in the layer in which the storm arose? . . . I formed hypothesis after hypothesis in order to reconcile these facts with hygrology,[26] and always in vain. During this labour of my imagination, it ran over and recalled to my mind all the instances of rain that I had observed in the mountains . . . Little by little these phenomena alone have confirmed everything that those I had observed on the mountains of Sixt had given me a glimpse of. *Rain is not the direct inverse of evaporation*; such is the general conclusion to which I have been led by this examination.[27]

There is little doubt that Deluc was misled to some extent by his hygrometer, which was imprecise, had a large temperature-coefficient, and, above all, was very sluggish. But he believed it, and these observations fixed his approach to meteorology for life.

We cannot traverse step by step the long and winding staircase

[25] *Idées*, ¶ 538.
[26] *Hygrologie:* Deluc's term for the physics of water vapour.
[27] *Idées*, ¶ 564. (Italics after Deluc.)

of argument by which Deluc finally arrives at his explanation of the cause of rain, but some of the main steps must be mentioned. One of the first things he had to do was to demolish the idea that water *dissolves* in air when it evaporates,[28] an idea that had outlived its usefulness but was held tenaciously by many people, especially chemists. He succeeded without much difficulty in showing it to be at least superfluous,[29] but seems not to have convinced all his critics.

De Saussure in his *Essais sur l'hygrométrie* had pointed out some of the mechanisms that might contribute to the formation of rain,[30] such as convection and the bringing in of air of a different temperature by the winds. He was hampered – as was Deluc – by the extreme complexity of mountain weather; and he did not know that rising air must cool. For these reasons he was not able to give a coherent theory of rain. Nevertheless Deluc used up many pages of the *Idées* in combating De Saussure's explanations, denying again and again the possibility of vertical currents, and refusing to believe that warm, moist winds could be cooled off quickly enough to produce the abundant rains that are observed.[31] He saw that a little rain could form at the interface where saturated air coming from the south 'passes over or under' a colder current; but he did not believe that there could be very much.[32] Again the clue, the cooling inseparably associated with ascent, is missing.

A further difficulty was the relatively small amount of water that the atmosphere would hold in the state of vapour. De Saussure had given a mean figure of 10 grains per cubic foot. Somehow neither De Saussure nor anyone else at the time seemed to realize that this was really a good deal, amounting to more than $\frac{1}{4}$ inch of precipitated water in a layer 1,000 feet thick. De Saussure did, however, point out that the amount of water in clouds could be much greater than that contained in the air as vapour.[33]

The clouds frequently dissipate after sunset, and dew begins to fall. As it is impossible to believe, says Deluc, that the layers of air

[28] See p. 28 above.   [29] *Idées*, ¶ 550–5.
[30] De Saussure, *Essais sur l'hygrométrie*. Neuchâtel, 1783, pp. 261 ff.
[31] Deluc, *Idées*, ¶ 571.   [32] *Ibid.*, ¶ 574.   [33] *Essais*, pp. 268–70.

in which the clouds float are warmed at this time, so as to cause the clouds to vanish, he is led to the conclusion that the appearance and disappearance of clouds is 'absolutely independent of the hygro-scopic state of the air'.[34] He then notes that when clouds are present they seem constantly to be evaporating and renewing themselves; and this leads him to one of his analogies:

> Observing these metamorphoses of one and the same cloud, nothing represents them more exactly for me than the idea of an invisible boiler suspended in the air, with water boiling violently in it. This image is too perfect a symbol of what is then observed for there not to be some analogy in the causes; that is to say, some metamorphosis of substance. This is what has led me to think that there is really a general source of vapours in the air, which furnishes them in certain circumstances; that these vapours are produced in the place where a cloud is formed; that while vapours continue to form, clouds subsist and even increase in size, though all the while evaporating; and that when the clouds dissipate it is because their evaporation is not replaced by the formation of new vapours.[35]

Rain clouds, he goes on, differ from others in that so much vapour is being formed that the vesicles come into contact and unite, finally breaking like large soap-bubbles and leaving drops. The drops sweep up more new vesicles on the way down. It seems certain to Deluc that even in an extended rain 'the vapours of which it is formed did not exist before the appearance of the clouds; and they only arise successively during the existence of these and the fall of the rain'.[36]

He returns again and again to the task of disproving the 'solution' theory of evaporation, even in the modified form given by De Saussure, and misinterprets the latter as supposing that water vapour exists in the same proportion to the air at all heights. De Saussure did not, of course, believe anything so obviously contrary to experience; but such an idea ought to be a logical consequence of a theory that assimilates the 'solution' of water in air to that of solids in liquids. We shall see that Deluc's critics wrongly made much of the 'solution' theory, instead of attacking him at his weak points, his fondness for

[34] Deluc, *Idées*, ¶ 606.   [35] *Ibid.*, ¶ 617.   [36] *Ibid.*, ¶ 625.

unsupported analogy and his readiness to postulate unobserved and even *a priori* unobservable substances.

Finally after about two hundred pages he comes to his great 'discovery'. From a consideration of long spells of fine weather, in which evaporation goes on without ceasing, he has come to the conclusion that so much water cannot possibly conceal itself in the upper atmosphere in the form of vapour. So:

> The evaporated water hides itself in the atmosphere under the appearance of some gaseous fluid (*fluide aëriforme*); for this is the only way in which it can escape its pressure, growing upon it as it accumulates, and the great differences of temperature to which it is subjected.[37]

But from time to time it resumes its watery form in some layer of air, and vapour is rapidly produced, saturation, cloud, and rain resulting. This is his great 'discovery'; the inter-convertibility of air and water.

This discovery, he would have us believe, was made by considering meteorological phenomena; but he could form no idea about the mechanism of such a process. When he came to England in 1773, he soon met Joseph Priestley and became fascinated by his experiments on gases. In 1782 he was told of the formation of water by the burning of 'inflammable air' in 'dephlogisticated air'. He expresses his delight in a way that rather gives the show away:

> I was struck by this discovery to the highest degree. The idea of water in any aërial form whatever was, to me, what a meeting with sea-birds[38] would be to sailors who have lost their compass and are searching blindly for the shore.[39]

But there was much more to come. In April 1783 Priestley made some ingenious experiments with an earthenware retort, in which it first appeared that water was being entirely transformed into air.[40] As he reported in his published paper, more refined experiments later convinced him that he had been dealing with differential transpiration through the porous vessel; but in the meantime Watt, who thought he had reason to believe that water could be made into a

---

[37] *Ibid.*, ¶ 672.   [38] *Oiseaux de mer;* but he probably meant land-birds.
[39] *Idées,* ¶ 675.   [40] Priestley, *Phil. Trans.* 73 (1783), 398–434.

permanent gas, undertook to interpret Priestley's experiments with the earthenware retort. At the end of a letter to Priestley dated 26 April 1783, Watt wrote:

> All that I conceive to be new in this paper is the Idea, First that Dephlogisticated air is composed of Water deprived of its Phlogiston, and united to a greater Quantity of Latent heat than it contains in the form of Water or of Steam; secondly that Water is pure air deprived of part of its latent heat and united to Phlogiston; and the application of your Experiments to prove these Hypotheses.[41]

Deluc was of course aware of Priestley's new interpretation of his experiments, but refused to believe in it. At any rate, water is composed of two gases, and at the end of his version of the story or the discovery of this fact, he exults:

> Such is the history of the first appearance of water in the form of air ... I regard this discovery as the dawn of a great day for meteorology. Less than six years ago, anyone who had said that water could exist in the form of air would have been thought a visionary.[42]

I shall not follow Deluc through the jungle of pneumatic chemistry to which he devotes forty pages at this point, and which seems to be designed to show that the higher the temperature at which organic substances are burned, the greater the amount of water produced. After this he comes back to the atmosphere, and immediately admits that one cannot suppose that the vanished water vapour is stored aloft as dephlogisticated air and inflammable air. If lightning did not explode such a mixture, the campfires of the mountaineers would.

This of course presents him with a problem. On the way to solving it, he manages to deny that atmospheric air is a mixture of two gases, in spite of Lavoisier, one of his arguments being that since 'vital air' and 'metaphitic air' have different specific gravities, they would separate out in calm weather. Atmospheric air is therefore 'a

---

[41] This letter was published by Robert E. Schofield in *Annals of Science* 10 (1954), 294–9. It is an important document in the controversy about the discovery of the composition of water (See J. R. Partington, *The composition of water*. London, 1928, Chap. IV).

[42] *Idées*, ¶ 691.

homogeneous expansible fluid, each particle of which contains all the ingredients we separate from it, and probably many others still unknown'.[43] He now comes to the point: it seems likely that the vapour, between the time it evaporates and the time it turns back into cloud, exists in the form of ordinary air. Ordinary air, he believes, contains both fire (*le feu*) and the ingredients of water. If this is so 'it depends only on some particular circumstance whether these ingredients, joined to fire, form water vapour or atmospheric air.'[44]

Grasping at bits of information – some of it due to experimental inadequacies – gleaned from the work of Cavendish and of Priestley, Deluc next guesses that the distinctive substance of nitrous air is contained in atmospheric air, and that it is principally by its presence that air differs from water vapour. If so, he thinks, the main problems of meteorology will have been solved.[45] But in support of these ideas it suddenly becomes very important to him to sustain, largely against De Saussure, his thesis that the rays of the sun do not heat things directly, but only by uniting with some substance to produce heat. He takes ninety pages for this argument, during which he again shows that he entirely disbelieves in the possibility of convection. Near the end of this discussion, which I shall not follow, we discover the reason for his insistence on this point:

> If now there is any foundation in the analytical comparison, which I made above, between aqueous vapours and atmospheric air, from which it results that one of their essential differences is that the air contains the principle of nitric acid – would it not be light which, while producing fire with one of the ingredients of water, also produces the substance that is the essential constituent of that acid?[46]

This is not quite the end of his speculations. Assuming his chemical explanation of rain, he asks why the clouds from which rain falls always form at some height above the plain, and often rather suddenly. Can we think, he asks,

> that the transformation of air into water vapour might be due to its being mixed with some sort of exhalation from the soil, which might

---

[43] *Ibid.*, ¶ 726.   [44] *Ibid.*, ¶ 730.
[45] Was he aware of the ideas of Mayow (see p. 73 above)?
[46] *Idées*, ¶ 807.

collect to a certain extent in some layer of air to produce this chemical operation in it?[47]

I have tried to give a brief summary of Deluc's complicated and extremely long-winded arguments for his theory of the inter-convertibility of water vapour and air. I wish to draw attention to the fact that the time was ripe for a theory of this sort, even before the sudden flowering of pneumatic chemistry in the hands of Cavendish and Priestley. For this was the day when heat was almost universally considered to be material, the more correct ideas of Boyle and Newton having been laid aside; light (following Newton this time) was corpuscular; and the 'electric fluid' was just as material as the others. As these were all substantial, they could be expected to enter into chemical combinations with more ponderable matter, or even with each other. At a critical moment in his cogitations, Deluc may well have been strongly influenced by a three-volume book by a compatriot of his, Jean Senebier, the Librarian of the Republic of Geneva; a book of which the title is an epitome of the speculations of the time.[48] Senebier's own extensive researches had made him certain that 'light is not merely the oscillation of an ethereal fluid [Huygens was not quite forgotten], but is truly a compound (*un composé*) of little bodies, which certainly combine with bigger ones ...'[49] Again,

> Fire, electricity, phlogiston, and light combine to a greater or lesser extent with substances exposed to their action, and can be contained in these substances in such a way that their presence is not suspected. But they can appear at any moment when the circumstances present themselves that are necessary to bring them into view.[50]

One can imagine the effect of this heady stuff, plus all the new gases found by Priestley, on anyone as ready as Deluc to form hypotheses.

Deluc was certainly a meteorologist before – and after – he was a chemist. By 1790 he was writing to La Métherie, then editor of the journal *Observations sur la physique*, that his study of meteorological phenomena has led him to abandon the opinion that water is formed

---

[47] *Ibid.*, ¶ 835.

[48] Jean Senebier, *Mémoires physico-chymiques, sur l'influence de la lumière solaire pour modifier les êtres des trois règnes de la nature* [etc.], 3 vol., Geneva 1782.

[49] *Ibid.*, I, 246.   [50] *Ibid.*, I, 256.

by the union of 'vital air' and 'inflammable air', and (as we have seen) the opinion that air is a mixture of two gases.[51] Since he has convinced himself that water vapour changes into air, it is unreasonable to have it changed into two kinds of air. He has to suppose that there are several unknown aerial fluids (of low specific gravity, for they are found at high levels), which could have their origins in various soils, and be carried long distances by the wind. The fall of the barometer indicates that the specific gravity of the air has decreased, and as there is not enough vapour to produce this effect, it must be due to these gases. So must the anomalies found in barometric hypsometry. Another piece of evidence for these hypothetical substances is given by 'the instrument improperly named the eudiometer', which shows that the 'residue of atmospheric air' is sometimes greater on the mountains. No one seemed to realize how inaccurate eudiometry was at this period.

In another paper[52] Deluc goes after Lavoisier and the 'new chemists', correctly objecting to Lavoisier's distinction between water vapour produced by boiling water (an elastic fluid) and that produced in air at lower temperatures. Lavoisier says the latter is dissolved. But Deluc tries to prove that air is not a mixture of gases, but a homogeneous substance; and then makes a bold sally into enemy territory on the subject of acids, maintaining

> that there exists an absolutely intangible substance to which all the phenomena of acidity are due, and other substances also entirely intangible which, united to the first, form the different acids. These substances, themselves impalpable, manifest themselves only when they become attached to the molecules of some liquid.[53]

In such obscure subjects, he says, it is permissible to make hypotheses, 'provided that they are left to the judgment of time'. This is the man who in another paper denounced Lavoisier for publishing as facts what were really only hypotheses.[54] In this 1791 paper he refers to the new chemists as *néologues*, and again summarizes his theories about rain in order to refute the new chemistry.

[51] Deluc, *Obs. sur la phys.* 36 (1790), 363–79.
[52] Deluc, *Obs. sur la phys.* 36 (1790), 276–90. [53] *Ibid.*, p. 288.
[54] Deluc, *Obs. sur la phys.* 39 (1791), 117–31.

126

Papers on meteorology became full of chemistry in the 1790s. Erasmus Darwin, the first of the members of the Lunar Society to be converted to the new chemistry,[55] wrote a long note on wind in his scientific poem *The Botanic Garden*. In this he refers to 'our yet imperfect knowledge of the means by which great regions of air are suddenly produced or suddenly destroyed.'[56] After a long description of all known and many hypothetical reactions between the 'oxygene' and 'azote' of the air, and the land, the sea, animals, and plants, and some references to the experiments of Lavoisier and of Priestley, Darwin speculates that there is 'an *officina aeris*, a shop where air is both manufactured and destroyed', in the polar regions. His wild guesses about the mechanism of these supposed processes are fascinating, but rather too long to be included here.

Deluc could scarcely have expected that his revolutionary theory would escape criticism. De Saussure, to whom he had been extremely unfair, was concerned to defend his hygrometer,[57] but made no reference to his theory of rain other than to point out that they both believed that water had to be evaporated by *le feu*.

A more serious critic was Johann Tobias Mayer the younger, of Erlangen,[58] in a paper that is interesting for two reasons: first because of its title, which shows that the new chemistry was becoming thought of as 'French chemistry'; and secondly, because it suggested a neat escape from Deluc's conclusions even without reference to convection, advection, or cooling by ascent. After water has been acted on by heat, argues Mayer, it attaches itself to the molecules of air (*an die Luftteilchen*). In this state it does not affect the hygrometer; indeed, 'the air can be saturated with water, and the hygrometer nevertheless show complete dryness'.[59] This, he says, is because the air attracts the water much more strongly than hygroscopic substances do.

Besides this attached water, there is also water mechanically

[55] Schofield, *The Lunar Society*, p. 297.

[56] E. Darwin, *The botanic garden; a poem, in two parts* [etc]. London 1789 and 1791. Additional note xxxiii to 'The Economy of Vegetation', p. (79).

[57] H. B. De Saussure, *Défense de l'hygromètre à cheveu, pour servir de suite aux essais sur l'hygrométrie*. Geneva, 1788.

[58] J. T. Mayer Jr., 'Etwas über den Regen, und Herrn de Luc's Einwurfe gegen die französische Chemie.' *Gren.'s J. der Phys.* 5 (1792), 371–83.

[59] *Ibid.*, p. 375.

dispersed in the air. This last, which is shown by the hygrometer, is the only water that can be precipitated by a change in temperature. As to the cause of heavy rain, only a change in the attractive force between the air and the water can release enough of the latter; but he does not know what changes this attraction. 'Without doubt electricity and light have a part in it. But who knows all the other finely divided substances that may be contained in air?'[60] It is clear that the difference between Mayer's theory and Deluc's is mainly that the latter wanted water to change into air, while the former would have it stick to the air-molecules.

Immediately after this the argument about Deluc's theory became almost inextricably mixed up with that about phlogiston and the *französische Chemie*, at least as far as German writers are concerned.[61] One of the most determined of these was the well-known physicist, satirist, and all-round *littérateur* Georg Christoph Lichtenberg, then Professor of Physics at Göttingen. He wrote a good deal on this subject, his first considerable contribution being in a preface on the 6th edition of J. C. P. Erxleben's *Anfangsgrunde der Naturlehre*.[62] In this brilliant and frankly nationalistic attack on the new chemistry, he uses Deluc's theory as a stick to beat the French with. Lichtenberg maintains that the arguments of Deluc's detractors are 'all pure opinion based on analogy and presumption', but quite fails to see that Deluc's theory is in exactly the same category.

One of Lichtenberg's victims was a private scholar from Rostock, John Dietrich Otto Zylius. Zylius had written to Gren's *Journal* in much the same vein as Mayer, though apparently independently.[63] In the second of these papers Zylius accuses Deluc of arguing in a circle; he wants to know:

> how it was possible for Deluc to conclude from the dryness of his hygrometer, without begging the question, that water vapour is not

[60] *Ibid.*, p. 376.

[61] Professor Partington says that 'the German chemists were just as ready to adopt the new views as any' (*A Short history of chemistry*, 3rd ed., p. 136). I am constrained to regard this as an overstatement; anti-French (or perhaps anti-Jacobin) feelings are obvious in the German periodical literature of the time.

[62] Göttingen, 1794, pp. xxi–xlvii.

[63] Zylius, *Gren's J. der Phys.* 6 (1792), 195–205; 8 (1794), 51–64.

dissolved, in view of the fact that while it was dissolved, the hygro-meter could not show its presence.[64]

In 1794 the Berlin Academy of Sciences, sensing the wide interest in the matter, offered a prize for the best examination of Deluc's theory. Zylius entered the only essay[65] and therefore, as we are told in the Academy's extensive preface, could not get the money. The Academy expected to receive a number of entries, but in any event they are circulating this one quickly, for it is important. If Deluc is right, 'then according to one of our most acute physicists [Lichten-berg] the antiphlogistic system of the French cannot be maintained, and at least in chemistry the counter-revolution has succeeded.'[66] This suggests anti-Jacobin sentiments rather than francophobia, and indeed it is interesting that the terms of the competition, printed on page 1 of the essay, are in French. We must remember that it was a *Royal* Academy. If they had hoped for a defence of Deluc, Zylius must have disappointed them.

Two questions are examined in the essay: do Deluc's observa-tions suffice to overthrow the 'solution theory'? and if so, can the change of vapour into air, and air again into cloud and rain, be physically demonstrated?

Zylius's negative answer to the first question rests on the theorem that if vapour is dissolved, the hygrometer will not reveal its pres-ence. His answer to the second begins with an observation that must occur to any twentieth-century reader of the *Idées*:

> . . . the first germ of this theory lies entirely and only *in the necessity of finding a cause of the phenomena.*[67]

He goes on to say that Deluc has not adduced a single fact to show how vapour can be changed into air, and complains of the complexity of Deluc's hypotheses, and especially of his introduction of com-pletely unknown substances.

[64] *Gren's J. der Phys.* 8, p. 56.
[65] J. D. O. Zylius, *Prüfung der neuen Theorie des Herrn de Lüc* (sic) *vom Regen und seiner daraus abgeleitete Einwürfe gegen die Auflösungstheorie. Eine von der konigl. preuss. Akademie der Wissenschaften zu Berlin gekrönte Preisschrift* [etc.]. Berlin 1795.
[66] *Ibid.*, p. iv.
[67] *Ibid.*, p. 77. The italics are from Zylius.

Lichtenberg was furious, and wrote a fair-sized book[68] in defence of Deluc and of the hygrometer, using his immense literary ability to treat Zylius (who ever heard of him, anyway?) very badly indeed. The associated snobbery is made very clear by the presence of an appendix in which Lichtenberg argues very politely indeed with 'Herr Hofrath Mayer' about the paper the latter published in 1792, which we have already noticed. Lichtenberg imagines Deluc asking himself what has become of the 'latent water' that no longer affects the hygrometer, and answering, 'It has been turned into air, because after all my efforts I find nothing else.'[69] One might object that the problem of the missing jewel-box could be 'solved' in exactly the same way.

Zylius did not take Lichtenberg's attack lying down, but wrote two articles about it,[70] unfortunately when his tormentor could no longer read them. In view of these it is a little hard to believe Deluc's later statement[71] that in 1799 Zylius had been to visit him and had gone away convinced.

In 1803 Deluc wrote another extensive work[72] with the definite purpose of demolishing the 'new chemical hypotheses' by way of his meteorological theories. This repeats most of the old arguments at enormous length, but with a changed emphasis. Naturally it was strongly criticised in the *Annales de Chimie*.[73] Unfortunately the anonymous reviewer chose the wrong places to attack Deluc's meteorology, and in his reply[74] Deluc really had much the better of the argument. Perhaps partly on account of this, his theory remained in favour in many quarters; he was, after all, the 'grand old man' of meteorology.[75] The 1797 edition of the *Encyclopaedia Britannica* took

[68] G. C. Lichtenberg, *Vertheidigung des Hygrometers und der Deluc'schen Theorie vom Regen*. (Posthumous, Ed. L. C. Lichtenberg & F. Kries.) Göttingen, 1800.

[69] *Ibid.*, p. 213.

[70] Zylius, *Ann. der Phys.* 5 (1800), 257–71; 8 (1801), 342–69.

[71] *Ann. de Chim.* 54 (1805), 285–6.

[72] *Introduction à la physique terrestre par les fluides expansibles*. Paris, 1803.

[73] Anon., *Ann. de Chim.* 48 (1803), 138–52, 273–83; 49 (1804), 84–94; 113–28; 225–38.

[74] Deluc, *Ann. de Chim.* 49 (1804), 306–27; 54 (1805), 156–95; 229–87.

[75] In 1805 the *Edinburgh Review* (Vol. 6, p. 515) referred to him editorially as a 'venerable philosopher'.

his theory as gospel. Even in 1820 the important German meteorologist Heinrich Wilhelm Brandes, who has been called the
father of synoptic meteorology, did not think it possible to disprove
theories like Deluc's, or at least to rid oneself of the idea that some
chemical process is going on;[76] and in 1828 the even more eminent
Heinrich Wilhelm Dove thought that Lichtenberg had the better of
it in his argument with Mayer.[77]

But there had been a serious and well-reasoned criticism of the
theory in 1814 by Chr. Leopold von Buch,[78] one of whose main
services was to demolish the idea that there could not be enough
vapour in the atmosphere, by showing that with a surface temperature of 22°R. (27.5°C.) and saturated air, there would be enough
water in the first 7,200 feet to make an inch and three quarters of
rain. And he had seen storm clouds higher than Mont Blanc. Deluc's
theory had quite lost its momentum by about 1835, when there was
something much sounder to replace it. Meteorology became a
branch of physics again.

It remains only to mention a peculiar theory put forward by a
professor at Riga, G. F. Parrot,[79] who believed that there were two
kinds of evaporation, physical and chemical. The amount of the
former depends on the temperature, that of the latter on the concentration of oxygen. Only the chemical evaporation produces a
real elastic fluid, and the formation of clouds and precipitation is
therefore able to circulate the oxygen of the atmosphere, as well as its
water. Parrot had been making experiments with a eudiometer of his
own invention. Carl Wilhelm Böckmann, Jr, had little trouble in showing that Parrot's chemical technique was at fault,[80] leading him to find
wide variations in oxgyen-content where none existed. The controversy continued with 'letters to the editor' (Gilbert) from K. F. Wrede[81]
and Parrot,[82] but no notice seems to have been taken of it elsewhere.

[76] H. W. Brandes, *Beiträge dur Witterungskunde* [etc.]. Leipzig, 1820; p. 345.
[77] H. W. Dove, *Ann. der Phys.* 89 (1828), 305.
[78] Von Buch, *Abh. K. Akad. Sci. Berlin* (1814–15), 94–100.
[79] Parrot, *Ann. der Phys.* 10 (1802), 166–218.
[80] Böckmann, *Ann. der Phys.* 10 (1802), 369–72; 11 (1802), 66–88.
[81] Wrede, *Ann. der Phys.* 12 (1802), 319–52.
[82] Parrot, *Ann. der Phys.* 13 (1803), 174–207; 244–50.

131

Chapter Seven

WATER VAPOUR IN THE NINETEENTH CENTURY

Il faut . . . s'imaginer que l'Univers infini n'est composé d'autre chose que de ces atomes infinis, très solides, très incorruptibles et très simples . . .

Cyrano de Bergerac (1619–1655),
HISTOIRE COMIQUE DES ÉTAT ET EMPIRE
DE LA LUNE ET DU SOLEIL. (Edition
J. J. Pauvert, Paris 1962, p. 99.)

In the chemical-meteorological church described in the previous chapter there was one unbeliever, and he a man generally thought of as a chemist. John Dalton wrote in 1793:

> Upon consideration of the facts, it appears to me, that evaporation and the condensation of vapour are not the effects of chemical affinities, but that aqueous vapour always exists as a fluid *sui generis*, diffused amongst the rest of the aerial fluids.[1]

Dalton was a countryman from Cumberland with very little formal education, who became a member of several great scientific societies, and died a famous man. His precise place in the history of science I leave to others.[2] Here we are concerned with his ideas regarding water vapour and their effect on the theories of rain. Yet it must be noted that he was studying meteorology before he got to be thought of as a chemist, and it appears that he even came to his atomic theory by way of speculation on the atmosphere.[3]

---

[1] John Dalton, *Meteorological Observations and Essays.* 2nd ed., Manchster and London, 1834, pp. 127–8. It is stated in the preface (p. XV) that the second edition 'is printed verbatim from the first [1793], both text and notes.'

[2] This is a difficult problem. See Frank Greenaway, 'The Biographical Approach to John Dalton,' *Mem. & Proc. Manchester Lit. & Phil. Soc.* Vol. 100 (1958–9).

[3] See Greenaway, pp. 75 ff.

In 1786 Joseph Priestley had written:

. . . when any two kinds of air, of the greatest different specific gravities, and without any known cause of attraction to each other, are mixed together in the same vessel, they are never separated by mere rest, but continue equally diffused through each other.[4]

Seven years later Dalton mentioned this statement,[5] and correctly speculated that a variation of moisture-content in the lower atmosphere can change the average specific gravity of the air-column and thus the reading of the barometer, without the necessity of supposing changes in the height of the atmosphere.

J. A. Deluc had also written in 1786 about the dependence of the maximum amount of water vapour on the temperature, and then:

This maximum of aqueous vapour is sensibly the same in every space, full of air or empty; this is what experiment shows us. From this we see that the minimum distance of the particles of vapour, which determines its maximum density, concerns only the vapour itself, independently of the aeriform fluids mixed with it.[6]

It is impossible to know whether Dalton had ever looked into the *Idées*, or even into Deluc's earlier work, the *Modifications*, though he mentions in the preface to the first edition of his *Observations and essays* that he had just seen a long article on the *Modifications* in an old *Monthly Review*. In any event he must have been thinking hard about vapour in the 1790s, and experimenting too, for at three meetings of the Manchester Literary and Philosophical Society on 2, 16 and 30 October 1801, he read a long paper which continued to provoke discussion and misunderstanding for more than sixty years.[7]

It is mainly the first part of the paper that interests us here. We shall set down his four 'laws' just as he wrote them:

[4] J. Priestley, *Experiments and observations relating to various branches of natural philosophy* [etc.] 3 vol., London, 1779; Birmingham 1781 and 1786; Vol. III, p. 390.

[5] *Met. obs. & essays*, 2nd ed., pp. 100–1.

[6] Deluc, *Idées sur la météorologie.* London 1786 and Paris 1787, ¶ 12.

[7] John Dalton, 'Experimental essays on the constitution of mixed gases; on the force of steam or vapour from water and other liquids in different temperatures, both in a Torricellian vacuum and in air; on evaporation; and on the expansion of gases by heat.' *Mem. Manchester Lit. & Phil. Soc.* 5 (1802), 535–602.

1. When two elastic fluids, denoted by A and B, are mixed together, there is no mutual repulsion amongst their particles; that is, the particles of A do not repel those of B, as they do one another. Consequently, the pressure or whole weight upon any one particle arises solely from those of its own kind.

2. The force of steam from all liquids is the same, at equal distances above or below the several temperatures at which they boil in the open air: and that force is the same under any pressure of another elastic fluid as it is in vacuo. Thus, the force of aqueous vapour of 212° is equal to 30 inches of mercury; at 30° below, or 182°, it is of half that force; and at 40° above, or 252°, it is of double the force; so likewise the vapour from sulphuric ether which boils at 102°, then supporting 30 inches of mercury, at 30° below that temperature it has half the force, and at 40° above it, double the force: and so in other liquids. Moreover, the force of aqueous vapour at 60° is nearly equal to $\frac{1}{2}$ inch of mercury, when admitted into a torricellian vacuum; and water at the same temperature, confined with perfectly dry air, increases the elasticity to just the same amount.

3. The quantity of any liquid evaporated in the open air is directly as the force of steam from such liquid at its temperature, all other circumstances being the same.

4. All elastic fluids expand the same quantity by heat: and this expansion is very nearly in the same equable way as that of mercury; at least from 32° to 212°. – It seems probable the expansion of each particle of the same fluid, or its sphere of influence, is directly as the quantity of heat combined with it; and consequently the expansion of the fluid as the cube of the temperature, reckoned from the point of total privation.[8]

This was indeed a tremendous budget to result from experiments of no great accuracy. Not all of it is relevant to our subject. The first part of law 2, for example, is inaccurate; Dalton had generalized wildly from experiments on only two liquids. The second part of this law, as we have seen, had been stated quite clearly by Deluc. The third law was not adequately supported. The fourth was important, and was given much more experimental support by Louis Joseph Gay-Lussac in the same year.[9] Gay-Lussac found that

[8] *Ibid.*, pp. 536–7.

[9] Gay-Lussac, *Ann. Chim. et Phys.* 43 (1802), 137–75. At this time he was still a student at the École nationale de Ponts et Chaussées.

air, hydrogen, oxygen, and nitrogen have the same expansion within a few parts in ten thousand, and also gave a critical historical survey, in which he noted that the chief source of error in such experiments is the presence of liquids or volatile solids in the apparatus. He stated that the physicist J. A. C. Charles had made successful experiments fifteen years before on oxygen, nitrogen, hydrogen, carbon dioxide, and air, obtaining similar results, but had never published them. Because of this statement the law concerning the thermal dilatation of gases is often called Charles's law.

In these remarks I have been referring, of course, only to the first sentence of Dalton's paragraph 4. The remainder is rather astonishing; Dalton was here speculating with reckless abandon, and it might seem that the 'sphere of influence' of each particle is scarcely consonant with his first law, to which we must now return.

In explaining this law of partial pressures, Dalton considers the two current views of the constitution of air: (1) that the two gases are merely mixed together, and (2) that they are in chemical combination. If they are mixed, he says, why do they not separate, the heavier below? If they are chemically combined, why do they not form 'nitric acid gas'? He will remove all such difficulties with his theory.

He bases this on two propositions, both considered axiomatic. The first is Boyle's law, though he does not mention Boyle. The second is that 'homogeneous elastic fluids are constituted of particles that repel one another with a force decreasing directly as the distance of their centres from each other [increases].'[10] For this he refers to Newton's *Principia*, Book II, Prop. 23, and seems to take it as proved that gases actually have this structure. Had he read to the end of the Scholium to this proposition, he would have found that Newton expressly denied knowledge of this point.[11] There is no question of interpretation here, for six years later Dalton declared that:

[10] Dalton, *Mem. Manchester Lit. & Phil. Soc.* 5 (1802), 542.

[11] 'But whether elastic fluids do really consist of particles repelling each other, is a physical question. We have here demonstrated mathematically the property of fluids consisting of particles of this kind, that hence philosophers may take occasion to discuss that question.' – *Principia*, Bk II, Prop. 23, Scholium, in Motte's translation as revised by Cajori, 1934.

Newton has demonstrated from the phenomena of condensation and rarefaction that elastic fluids are constituted of particles, which repel one another by forces which increase in proportion as the distance of their centres diminishes: in other words, the forces are reciprocally as the distances. This deduction will stand as long as the Laws of elastic fluids continue to be what they are. What a pity it is that all who attempt to reason, or to theorize respecting the constitution of elastic fluids, should not make themselves thoroughly acquainted with this immutable Law, and constantly hold it in their view whenever they start any new project![12]

What a pity it is that those who have been basking in the sunshine of Newton's genius should not at least read him carefully before going in at the deep end! It appears that at some later period Dalton must have looked into this matter again, for by 1826 he has realized that Newton did not infer that gases *must* consist of mutually repulsive particles.[13]

Let us go back to 1802. Assuming such a repulsion, he examines how it might apply to mixed gases, and considers four possibilities: (1) The particles of one may repel those of another with the same force as they repel those of their own kind. But if so, he says, they would separate out according to their specific gravities. (2) The particles of one may repel those of another with forces greater or less than they exert on their own kind. This hypothesis meets with the same objection. (3) There is a chemical affinity; this is objected to because it almost always results in a change of state or of volume or of both. (4) The particles of one gas may be entirely neutral, or inelastic, with respect to those of all the others. In the last case, he maintains, each elastic fluid will fill all the space, its partial pressure being proportional to its relative amount in the total.

Dalton was obviously delighted with this idea. The moment this hypothesis is admitted, he says:

> every difficulty vanishes, and every fact appears a simple and immediate consequence of it. The atmosphere, or to speak more properly the

[12] Dalton, *A new system of chemical philosophy*, Parts I and II. London, 1808, p. 168. Dalton's unwillingness to revise his books is shown by the fact that this statement is repeated verbatim in the 1842 edition, p. 168.
[13] Dalton, *Phil. Trans.* 116, Part II (1826), 174.

compound of atmospheres, may exist together in the most intimate mixture, without any regard to their specific gravities, and without any pressure upon one another. Oxygenous gas, azotic gas, hydrogenous gas, carbonic acid gas, aqueous vapour, and probably several other elastic fluids may exist in company under any pressure and in any temperature, whilst each of them, however paradoxical it may appear, occupies the whole space allotted to them all. For, the space with them all in it, is little more comparatively than a vacuum, such is the great tenuity of all elastic fluids.[14]

We now know, of course, that the hypothesis of the independence of the various gases was unnecessary. Dalton could have known it, too, if he had read Daniel Bernouilli's *Hydrodynamica*.[15] But nobody had paid any attention to the *Hydrodynamica*. What Dalton had fashioned might be called a static theory of gases, in contrast to the kinetic theory initiated by Bernouilli but only developed – re-invented, in fact – in the nineteenth century. Dalton's formulation itself might have done no harm to meteorology, but one of the consequences he drew from it did cause a great deal of confusion. This was in regard to the evaporation of water.

If all the other gases but water vapour were taken away, writes Dalton:

little addition would be made to the aqueous atmosphere, because it already exists in every place, almost entirely up to what the temperature will admit; the evaporation of water would be essentially the same in that case as at present; only the full effect would take place in less time. In short this notion of pressure preventing the evaporation of liquids, which seems to have been taken as an axiom by modern philosophers, has been the cause of more error and perplexity perhaps than any other ungrounded opinion.[16]

Much later in this long paper he says that the obstruction offered by the air to the evaporation of water 'is caused by the *vis inertiae* of the particles of air; and is similar to that which a stream of water meets in descending amongst pebbles'.[17]

[14] Dalton, *Mem. Manchester Lit. & Phil. Soc.* 5 (1802), 545.
[15] Strasbourg, 1738. See p. 29 above.
[16] Dalton, *Mem. Manchester Lit. & Phil. Soc.* 5 (1802), 548–9.
[17] *Ibid.*, p. 581.

It is most surprising that he did not see what it was that he was asserting: namely that the whole atmosphere is, 'in every place', almost saturated. What then constitutes dry weather or wet weather? He must be convicted of either woolly thinking or careless exposition in such a passage, which certainly did nothing to diminish the total quantity of 'error and perplexity' in this awkward subject. He did even more damage in the following year when he wrote:

> On my principle the density of the aqueous atmosphere at any height is totally independent of the density of the compound mass of air, and is to be ascertained by knowing the density of vapour at the earth's surface, and its specific gravity; in the same way as we would ascertain the density of the oxygenous or azotic atmospheres, or one of hidrogen, at any given height, having the like data.[18]

The strange thing is that the contradictions in all this seem to have escaped notice for some time, though his theory was given wide and favourable publicity.[19] The theory was at once criticized, however, by the adherents of the 'solution' theory of evaporation; indeed the quotation immediately above is from an answer to one of these, Richard Kirwan.[20] It was also attacked by those who, like the famous chemist Thomas Thomson, believed that air is a compound.[21] Dalton replied to Thomson in *Nicholson's Journal*,[22] complaining that he had been misunderstood.

Those who believed that air was a chemical compound received welcome support in 1804 from a man who certainly did not. On 16 September of that year Gay-Lussac made an astonishing if perhaps foolhardy balloon ascent in the cause of science, reaching an estimated altitude of 6,636 metres. Analyses of air taken from near the ground and at the top of the flight showed exactly the same content of oxygen, 21·49 per cent.[23]

As far as my reading goes, the first man to protest that Dalton's

[18] Dalton, *Nicholson's J.* (1803), 119–20.
[19] For example by L. W. Gilbert in his *Annalen der Physik*, 15 (1803), 25–70; he argued that the experiments of Clément and Désormes (*Ann. de Chimie* 42 (1802), 121–52) were in accord with it.
[20] *Phil. Mag.* 14 (1802), 143–8; 251–8.
[21] Thomson, *A system of chemistry*, 4 vol., Edinburgh, 1802, Vol. III, pp. 269–70.
[22] Vol. 3 (1802), 267–72.   [23] L. J. Gay-Lussac, *J. de Phys.* 59 (1804), 454–61.

ideas on mixed gases do not follow from Dalton's experiments was the unfortunate G. F. Parrot, who for once was right;[24] but nobody took any notice, unless it may have been Dalton himself, who in 1805 reported experiments with two vessels and a long glass tube to show the diffusion of gases against the force of gravity,[25] and used the results to explain the experiments of Priestley (1783) with a porous retort.[26] But still Dalton's theory had no experimental basis, and in 1807 J. G. Tralles objected that the inter-diffusion of gases was merely a consequence of their not filling all the available space, and could not furnish a proof of the theory.[27] He also contrasted the almost instantaneous rush of a gas into an empty space with the relatively slow diffusion of gases into one another; and adduced Gay-Lussac's balloon observations against Dalton's theory.

Another interesting difficulty came from acoustical theory, for Newton had shown that the speed of sound in a gas varies as the square root of the pressure and inversely as the square root of the density. It was therefore argued[28] that if Dalton's theory of independent atmospheres were correct, we should hear several sounds from one distant explosion, and several pitches at once from a wind instrument. The force of this argument was lessened by the fact that Newton's formula gave quite the wrong speed for sound, but in 1816, when Laplace corrected Newton's theory by making allowance for the fact that the rarefactions and compressions produced by the sound-wave are adiabatic,[29] satisfactory agreement with experiment was obtained.

Just at this time the kinetic theory of gases, long embalmed in Bernouilli's *Hydrodynamica*, had a resurrection almost as little noticed as its original birth. In complete independence of Bernouilli, John Herepath published papers in the *Annals of Philosophy* between 1816 and 1821 in which he derived the law of ideal gases and gave simple explanations of diffusion, changes of state, and the properties of sound. His papers were refused by the Royal Society, mainly

[24] Parrot, *Ann. der Phys.* 17 (1804), 82–101.
[25] Dalton, *Mem. Manchester Lit. & Phil. Soc.* 1 (1805), 259–70.
[26] See p. 122 above.   [27] Tralles, *Ann. der Phys.* 27 (1807), 400–48.
[28] *E.g.* by Johann Friedrich Benzenberg in *Ann. der Phys.* 42 (1812), 155–96.
[29] Laplace, *Ann. de Chim.* 3 (1816), 238–41.

because of the opposition of Sir Humphry Davy, then its president; and were forgotten until mentioned by J. P. Joule in 1848.[30] Meanwhile Dalton's theory naturally got into the textbooks, for example into John Frederic Daniell's *Meteorological essays and observations*,[31] though Daniell did see quite clearly that the amount of water vapour at any height must be limited by the temperature.

Dalton himself returned to the subject in 1826, showing by an imaginary experiment, though not very clearly, that the separate gases in the atmosphere should diminish at very different rates. But he admits at the end that all he has said applies to a quiescent atmosphere, and doubts whether the constitution of the actual atmosphere, always in motion, can be described theoretically.[32] As we shall see in Chapter eight, this scepticism was unjustified. In 1837 he published a continuation of this paper, detailing numerous experiments made between 1824 and 1835 on the composition of air taken at various elevations.[33] These showed only small variations, some certainly to be ascribed to experimental error. The paper contains the following sentence:

> It appears, however, that the disproportion of the two elements [oxygen and nitrogen] at different elevations is by no means as great as theory requires; and therefore we must conclude the unceasing agitation of the atmosphere by currents and counter-currents is sufficient to maintain an almost uniform mixture at the different elevations to which we have access.[34]

In view of this, and of the objections to his theory, it seemed mere stubborness to maintain it at all. He may in fact have been getting tired of it, for when in 1834 he reprinted his *Meteorological observations and essays* of 1793, verbatim, with only an 'appendix to the second edition' by way of revision, all he said about it was a passing reference to 'another essay' in which he had shown that 'one gas [is] as a vacuum to another in regard to their mutual diffusion'.[35]

Not long before he died he stated the theory of mixed gases in a modified form:

[30] Regarding Herepath see S. G. Brush, *Annals of Science* 13 (1957), 188–98.
[31] London, 1823, pp. 72 ff.   [32] Dalton, *Phil. Trans.* 116, part II (1826), 174–87.
[33] *Phil. Trans.* [127], (1837), 347–63.   [34] *Ibid.*, p. 356.
[35] *Meteorological observations and essays*, 2nd ed., p. 211.

1st. The diffusion of gases through each other is effected by means of the repulsion belonging to the homogeneous particles; or to that principle which is always energetic to produce the dilatation of the gas. 2nd. When two or more mixed gases acquire an equilibrium, the elastic energy of each against the surface of the vessel or of any liquid, is precisely the same as if it were the only gas present occupying the whole space, and all the rest were withdrawn.[36]

The reader may note that the first paragraph of the above quotation would allow for a kinetic theory of gases.

Meanwhile Dalton's theory continued to generate a good deal of argument. J. F. Benzenberg had been converted to it, and in 1830 wrote a fair-sized book in its defence,[37] in which he expressed his belief that, like Copernicus and Harvey, Dalton would eventually triumph. Benzenberg's specialty was barometric hypsometry, and he applied Dalton's theory to some old observations by D'Aubuisson (1809) and De Saussure, (1787), claiming that it made their results coincide with heights obtained trigonometrically. His results were far too close to be convincing, and are of interest only because they caused the formidable Karl Friedrich Gauss to smell a rat. He reviewed the book in the *Göttingische gelehrte Anzeigen*,[38] first showing that Benzenberg's calculations are faulty, and should actually lead to a difference of opposite sign, and then demonstrating that the accuracy of the whole process is far from sufficient to enable a decision to be made about Dalton's theory, in which Gauss clearly did not believe.

Nor did the able Scottish chemist Thomas Graham, who in 1834 established the laws of the diffusion and interchange of gases through a porous partition. The numerical results with various gases were found to be inconsistent with Dalton's theory.[39]

After all this the theory was plainly very ill; but it would not die, and it continued to bother the meteorologists, and even the astronomers. In a long discussion of astronomical refraction, J. B. Biot showed by numerical example that if the vapour pressure were a

[36] Dalton, *A new system of chemistry*, 1842, Part I, p. 191.
[37] Benzenberg, *Über die Dalton'sche Theorie*. Dusseldorf, 1830.
[38] December 1830, pp. 1945–56. The review is unsigned, but probably by Gauss.
[39] Graham, *Trans. Roy. Soc. Edinb.* 12 (1834), 222–58.

constant fraction of the total pressure at all heights, impossible values would soon be reached in ascending, unless the surface air were extremely dry.[40] This sort of reasoning went on for another quarter of a century, culminating in a brilliant paper by Lt-Col Richard Strachey, who examined Himalayan observations by Joseph Hooker, and some of his own, finding that the vapour pressure at 18,000 feet was only about a quarter as much as would be given by Dalton's theory, and that on the basis of a constant proportion of vapour the dew point would soon come to be higher than the temperature in an ascent.[41] His general conclusions were beautifully stated:

> We may therefore conclude generally, that the known diminution of temperature in the atmosphere is incompatible with the existence of so large a quantity of vapour in the upper strata as the theory in question demands; and, consequently, that the tensions observed at the surface are neither dependent on, nor balanced by, the pressure of the vapour in the higher parts of the atmosphere (in the way in which the entire barometric pressure depends on the weight of the whole superincumbent column of air), for this would be insufficient to produce them. To render an independent vapour atmosphere possible would indeed, require a fall of temperature in the air of about 1° for 1,500 feet, or less than a quarter of what really takes place.
>
> It will also follow that, as the tension of vapour at any point exceeds the sum of all the pressures of vapour above it, it must in part be due to the reaction of the air particles, which must therefore press upon the vapour, contrary to the supposition with which we started.[42]

The director of the Munich Observatory, Johann von Lamont, wrote a series of papers on the subject in the years 1860 to 1864.[43, 44, 45] By combining the results of meteorological observation with laboratory experiments of his own, he showed what Strachey had shown, but he also emphasized that there is no justification for

[40] Biot, *Additions à la Connaissance des Tems pour 1839*, pp. 29–31.
[41] Strachey, *Proc. Roy. Soc.* 11 (1861), 182–9.   [42] *Ibid.*, p. 185.
[43] *K. Bayerischen Akad. Wiss., Abh., math.-phys. Kl.* 8, pt. 1 (1860), 181–239.
[44] *Ann. der Phys.* 118 (1863), 168–78. Translation in *Proc. British Meteorol. Soc.* 1 (1863), 310–18.
[45] *Zeits. für Math. & Phys.* 9 (1864), 439–47. Translation in *Proc. British Meteorol. Soc.* 2 (1864), 265–74.

assuming that water vapour ever has time to reach a state of equilibrium in spite of the presence of the air. The results of reading a hygrometer in any given place show nothing more than the local humidity of the air, and nothing regarding the distribution of water vapour in the vertical. Lamont's papers are not very clear either in German or English, but he performed a valuable service in pointing out the kinetic aspect of the matter.[46]

The immediate sequel is amusing. It started with a very bad-tempered attack on Lamont by J. C. Bloxham,[47] apparently on patriotic grounds, which merely made it quite clear that he had not understood what Lamont was objecting to. The Astronomer Royal, Sir George Biddell Airy, perhaps appealed to by the editor – Lamont was an astronomer – tried to smooth things over.[48] It is questionable whether he entirely realized what the fuss was about, but he did make one salutary remark:

> ... the hygrometer showing a great density of vapour near the ground, it has been supposed that the density of vapour in every stratum above it can be computed from that lower density by the same laws as if vapour were the only gas above the ground, disseminating itself by the ordinary laws of gaseous dissemination [i.e. diffusion]. I do not know whether any writer has expressed the principle so broadly as I have stated it; but I think that some have come very near to it, and I have no doubt whatever that it is the tacit idea which guides many meteorologists.[49]

Poor Bloxham came back, much more politely.[50] He now understands that the upper strata may be very moist when the lower are dry, and vice versa, but he will not criticise Dalton. 'So far as I comprehend, it would be an egregious error to assume that Dalton's law, as English meteorologists understand it, is false, nevertheless.'[51] I am almost ashamed to reveal that in the same paper Bloxham had suggested an 'electric control' of the 'viscosity' of the aqueous vapour.

[46] Particulars of other experimental and statistical researches, all pointing to the inadequacy of Dalton's theory, will be found in H. H. Hildebrandsson & L. Teisserenc de Bort, *Les bases de la météorologie dynamique*. Paris, 1907, Vol. 1, pp. 157 ff.

[47] *Proc. British Meteorol. Soc.* 1 (1863), 362–5.   [48] *Ibid.* 1 (1863), 365–6.

[49] *Ibid.*, p. 366.   [50] *Ibid.*, 2 (1864), 41–47.   [51] *Ibid.*, p. 44.

In Lamont's final reply[52] he points out once more that it does make a difference to meteorology whether or not the atmospheres of air and vapour are independent of one another.

But Dalton's theory, though scotched, was not quite dead, and the famous Austrian meteorologist J. von Hann, director of the *Zentralanstalt für Meteorologie und Geodynamik* at Vienna, still found it desirable in 1874 to quote Strachey and Lamont.[53] He also used various observations in the Himalayas, in Armenia, on Teneriffe, and in the Alps, as well as balloon flights by Welsh and by Glaisher, and worked out an empirical formula for the relation between vapour pressure and height, which confirmed Strachey's results very closely. The actual formula need not concern us; but one of its consequences is of great interest. It turns out – as indeed Strachey had noted – that 9/10 of all the water vapour in the atmosphere is below 20,000 feet; and therefore high mountain ranges form an efficient barrier to the transport of vapour.

While some British meteorologists had been mistakenly defending Dalton, physicists and mathematicians in Great Britain and abroad had been busy in their laboratories and at their desks. Many determinations of maximum vapour pressure as a function of temperature were made, with increasing precision, from Schmidt[54] and Dalton[55] to the magnificent investigations of Henri Victor Regnault, which remained definitive for many years.[56] Very early in this game the mathematicians began to devise interpolation formulae for the relation. J. von Soldner was one of the first to do this,[57] but by 1833 Egen[58] was able to review twenty-nine such formulae, adding four of his own.

The presence of air was supposed to have no effect on the maximum vapour pressure, but Regnault challenged this conclusion in 1854.[59] In every one of ninety-one experiments, the saturation vapour

[52] See note 45.   [53] J. von Hann, *Zeits. österr Ges. Meteorol.* 9 (1874), 193–200.
[54] G. G. Schmidt, *Gren's neue J. der Phys.* 4 (1797), 251–319.
[55] Dalton, *Mem. Manchester Lit. & Phil. Soc.* 5 (1802), 535–602.
[56] H. V. Regnault, *Compt. Rend.* 20 (1845), 1120–66; 1220–37.
[57] Soldner, *Ann. der Phys.* 17 (1804), 44–81.
[58] P. N. C. Egen, *Ann. der Phys.* 27 (1833), 9–40.
[59] Regnault, *Compt. Rend.* 39 (1854), 301–13; 345–57; 397–409.

pressure was somewhat less in air than in a vacuum. What is interesting to me about this paper is that for Regnault 'Dalton's law' refers merely to the additivity of the vapour pressures and gas pressures in the same space, with no reference whatever to the independence of the molecules.[60] The great French experimenter would no doubt have been amazed if he had been aware of all the arguments going on far below him on the plain around Olympus.

It was noted above that John Herepath had made a fruitless attempt to interest people in the kinetic theory of gases. In 1828 Robert Brown discovered the ceaseless random motion of very small particles in a liquid, which would forever be called the Brownian motion. In 1851 James Prescott Joule, more famous for his determination of the mechanical equivalent of heat, gave a rough proof that Boyle's law is consistent with the hypothesis that gases are composed of particles constantly flying about in every direction with great speed.[61] This was somewhat improved upon by A. Krönig five years later,[62] and in 1857 R. J. E. Clausius[63] gave the kinetic theory of gases its first clear statement, taking into account translation, rotation, and vibration of the molecules. More to our present purpose, he gave a kinetic theory of evaporation. Molecules have a certain mean speed; but there are faster and slower ones, and the more energetic will leave the surface of a liquid and fly about in the space above it. Any striking the liquid again will go back. Evaporation continues until the number leaving and the number returning are in balance, and the higher the temperature, the more will be in the space at any moment.

The kinetic theory was further refined by many workers during the rest of the century. By 1886 W. Ferrel was able to write in an official report[64] that it could furnish a complete explanation of the

[60] Ibid., p. 397. Dalton has received more than his due, for this seems to be the modern interpretation of 'Dalton's law'.

[61] Joule, Mem. Manchester Lit. & Phil. Soc. 9 (1851), 107–14.

[62] Krönig, Ann. der Phys. 99 (1856), 315–22.

[63] Clausius, Ann. der Phys. 100 (1857), 353–80. Translated in Phil. Mag. 14 (1857), 108–27.

[64] Ferrel, 'Recent Advances in Meteorology [etc.]', U.S. War Dept., Ann. Rep. Chief Signal Officer, Washington 1886, Appendix 71.

phenomenon of partial pressures, correctly described by Dalton but incorrectly explained. Dalton, said Ferrel, was wrong on two points: the speed at which the distribution of the various gases in a mixture would take place, and the reason for it. His first mistake prevented him seeing that in the atmosphere such a state of equilibrium would never even approximately occur.

Chapter Eight

NINETEENTH-CENTURY THEORIES OF RAIN

We cannot assume that any condition of weather, normal or abnormal, can be ascribed to a single cause.

Sir Napier Shaw, MANUAL OF
METEOROLOGY, Vol. I, Cambridge,
1926, p. 113.

1. INTRODUCTION

By the year 1800, our subject was in a peculiarly unsatisfactory condition. Most of the ideas that have since proved fruitful, such as the formation of ascending currents and the cooling of air by ascent, had been almost forgotten; and ideas with little or no future had taken their place, such as the pseudo-chemical theory of Deluc that we studied in Chapter Six. The eighteenth-century habit of system-building, of which Deluc provided a particularly flamboyant example, was only just beginning to be replaced by an appropriate humility in the face of experimental data—or the lack of them.

It is also, perhaps, unfortunate that the most active meteorologists in the last half of the eighteenth century were from the region of the Alps. Mountain weather is often spectacular, and it may have been this that led to the activity in question; but it is also very complicated, or rather the presence of the mountains makes it more difficult to disentangle the physical processes involved. It is notable that the first real progress in the nineteenth century came from countries like the United States where the relief is much less prominent in relation to the size of the region that can be studied. This renaissance was also dependent on the possibility of well-organized synoptic networks; and while the United States was not the first country to have synoptic meteorological observations, it was the first to have them in fair numbers over a very large region.

The theoretical progress in our subject during the nineteenth century was founded on developments in thermodynamics. When these were properly understood, a great step was at once taken towards understanding the various large-scale mechanisms that produce rain. Only towards the end of the period was there much progress in understanding the small-scale processes involved. This subject, which has expanded immensely in our time, will be dealt with briefly in the last two sections of this chapter.

2. THE FIRST QUARTER-CENTURY

Immediately after 1800 most of the relevant activity seems to have been concentrated in the British Isles, and it would have been pleasant to report that it was of much importance, apart from the work of Dalton, which was dealt with in Chapter seven. Luke Howard deserves and receives our lasting gratitude for producing the first useful classification of cloud-forms, but he was not competent enough in the exact sciences to make any notable contribution to the theory of rain. He never quite divested himself of a belief in the importance of electricity in its production: 'rain is in almost every instance the result of the electrical action of clouds upon each other.'[1] However, electricity is only 'a secondary agent, which modifies the effect of the two grand predisposing causes – a falling temperature and the influx of vapour'.[2] Eight years later he says that the form of cirrus reflects the arrangement of electrical currents flowing in the upper air.[3] He retained his belief in the importance of electricity for the production of rain, though always as a secondary agent.[4] He was clear about the formation of cumuli in an ascending current, but in the absence of any knowledge of the necessary connexion between ascent and cooling, he thought that the ascending vapour 'changes its climate, and arrives among air at a lower temperature'.[5] This is an instance of the widespread belief that vapour can move rapidly upwards quite independently of the motion of the rest of the air in

[1] Howard, *Phil. Mag.* 17 (1803), 9.   [2] *Ibid.*, p. 11.
[3] Howard, *Nicholson's J.* 30 (1811), 57–58.
[4] Howard, *The Climate of London.* 2nd ed., 3 vols., London, 1833, Vol. I, p. 128.
[5] Howard, *Nicholson's J.* 30 (1811), 51.

which it is contained. It is probable that Dalton's statement of the independence of gaseous atmospheres kept this erroneous idea alive for a number of years.

Chemists like Kirwan and Thomas Thomson refused to abandon the idea that water dissolves in air. This was to prove a dead-end street, and could only lead to statements like this one, by Kirwan:

> When the barometer rises, clouds are partly dissolved, as dense air is a better solvent than rarer air, and partly rise higher in consequence of the increased specific gravity of the inferior air; when the barometer falls, the contrary takes place.[6]

A more fruitful, if still highly empirical approach was made by Sir Humphry Davy, who emphasized the natural decrease of temperature with height, but somehow managed to confuse it with the effect of mere remoteness from the ground:

> When air is made to expand . . . a diminution of temperature is occasioned . . . on these ideas, it is easy to account for the correspondence between the diminution of the temperature of the atmosphere and its height; for if it be conceived that the capacity [for heat] of air rarefied by heat, increases as it ascends, the heat of temperature which was the cause of its ascent must, at a certain elevation, become heat of capacity: and the higher and more rarefied the air, the more it is removed from the source of heat, and the greater its power of diminishing temperature.[7]

Davy was a chemist, and we may treat this as a mere incident in a chemical book. No such excuse can be made for Sir John Leslie, of whose extraordinary unreliability in meteorological matters we have already seen an instance.[8] In a book published in 1813,[9] interesting to the historian of meteorological instruments, we find Davy's ideas taken over and developed into a qualitative statement of convective equilibrium:

> The increased capacity [for heat] of rarefied air is the true cause of the cold which prevails in the higher regions of the atmosphere. From the

---

[6] R. Kirwan, *Phil. Mag.* 14 (1802), 258.

[7] Davy, *Elements of chemical philosophy.* London, 1812, p. 90.

[8] See p. 81 above.

[9] Leslie, *A short account of experiments and instruments, depending on the relations of air to heat and moisture.* Edinburgh, 1813.

unequal action of the sun's rays and the vicissitudes of day and night, *a perpetual and quick circulation is maintained between the lower and the upper strata; and it is obvious that, for each portion of air which rises from the surface, an equal and corresponding portion must also descend.* But that which mounts up, acquiring an enlargement of capacity, has its temperature proportionally diminished; while the correlative mass falling down carries likewise its heat along with it, and, contracting its capacity, seems to diffuse warmth below.[10]

The portion that I have italicized is the clearest statement of the convective process that had been produced, as far as I am aware, up to that date. There had been much talk of 'ascending currents', but it was time that someone pointed out that what goes up must come down. It would be an anachronism to find in passages such as this an intuition of the conservation of energy, but of course the varying 'capacity' for heat was destined to be translated into the terms of thermodynamics.

I have the impression that Leslie seldom referred back to what he had already written. At any rate, farther along in the book, in support of Hutton's theory of rain, he writes:

Air in cooling becomes ready to part with its moisture. But how is it ever cooled in the free atmosphere? Only by the contact or commixture surely with a colder portion of the same fluid.[11]

He then proceeds to show that very little of the total moisture in two masses of air at ordinary temperature will be condensed, on Hutton's principles, by mixing; but he asks us to suppose two currents blowing in opposite directions and grazing each-other along their common boundary, and says that these might furnish a good deal of rain. There seems to be a fallacy here, as if he thought that all the rain produced by a great extent of these currents would be concentrated in a relatively small area. And a few pages farther on we are pulled up short by the following passage:

In fine calm weather, after the rays of the declining sun have ceased to warm the surface of the ground, the descent of the higher mass of air gradually chills the undermost stratum . . .[12]

[10] *Ibid.*, p. 11–12. Italics added.   [11] *Ibid.*, p. 125.   [12] *Ibid.*, p. 132.

What has happened to the heat carried down by the falling air, and the contraction of its capacity? The truth seems to be that Leslie, a good laboratory man, was entirely lost in the open air.

It is interesting that the explanation of the low temperatures of the air near the ground at night was given in the very next year by William Charles Wells, of whom we shall hear much in Chapter Nine. The explanation was, of course, invisible radiation.[13]

The *courant ascendant* began to be fashionable. In 1816 Leopold von Buch told a meeting of the Berlin Academy of Sciences that 'the principle of the ascending current of air should really be called the key to the whole science of meteorology'.[14] Bellani in 1817 quoted Davy with approval on the subject.[15] It is therefore the more surprising that in 1820 Heinrich Wilhelm Brandes, a considerable figure in the history of meteorology,[16] while understanding that cumulus clouds are formed by the convection of moist air upwards, doubted that the vapour is condensed by being mixed with the cold upper air, as was commonly supposed,[17] and was of the opinion that electricity may have a great deal to do with it. He also believed that for the production of continuous rain, especially heavy or lasting rain, it is necessary to have two layers of cloud, which interact.[18]

An even greater meteorologist – or perhaps I should say climatologist – than Brandes was Heinrich Wilhelm Dove, whom we shall meet again below. It is evident that Dove, at least for many years, never really understood adiabatic cooling by ascent. I suppose that the phenomenon can only be understood by doing the mathematics of the process, and these men were not of that type of mind.

The mathematics began to be done about 1823, when Siméon

[13] Wells, *An essay on dew and several appearances connected with it*. London, 1814. (2nd ed., 1815, 3rd ed., 1818. Reprinted 1866. It is this reprint that I have used.)

[14] Quoted by S. Günther, *Gerlands Beitr. Geophys.* 5 (1903), 178. We shall see in Chapter X how von Buch made use of it in his theory of hail.

[15] Angelo Bellani, *Giornale di Fisica, Pavia* 10 (1817), 376.

[16] Credited with preparing the first synoptic weather charts (for the year 1783) in 1816. See K. Schneider-Carius, *Wetterkunde, Wetterforschung. Geschichte ihrer Probleme und Erkenntnisse in Dokumenten aus drei Jahrtausenden*. Freiburg & München, Karl Alber, 1955, pp. 156 and 200.

[17] H. W. Brandes, *Beiträge zur Witterungskunde*[etc.], Leipzig, 1820, pp. 314 ff.

[18] *Ibid.*, pp. 327–8.

Denis Poisson derived formulae for the relations between the temperature and pressure, or temperature and density, of a gas compressed or expanded adiabatically (i.e. with no loss or gain of heat).[19] It should be understood that these refer to unsaturated air only. It was soon realized, as we shall see, that saturated air must behave differently; but the mathematics of ascending saturated air was not worked out properly for many years.

3. THE CLASSIFICATION OF RAINS

As I have tried to show in earlier chapters, a belief that had greatly retarded the development of the theory of rain was the belief that all rains are produced in the same way. By about 1825 it had become evident to a few people that this was by no means the case. One of these was the young H. W. Dove, who received his Doctorate at Berlin in 1826[20] and immediately embarked on over 50 years of furious meteorological activity. He took as his main field of work a subject that would nowadays be called 'dynamic climatology', and his thinking was always statistical rather than physical. Because a model made by averaging a number of storms is never like any one of them, his theories of storms were never very helpful, but his authority was so very great that, in the words of some later meteorologists, they hindered the acceptance of more correct theories for about 30 years.[21] This climatological outlook is evident even in Dove's dissertation, and by 1828 it was fully established, and visible in the title of the paper we must now consider.[22] This paper performed the important service of classifying rains according to the method of their formation.

Precipitation, says Dove, 'must occur when the temperature of the air is lowered to the condensation point [dew point] of the water

[19] Poisson, *Ann. de Chim.* 23 (1823), 337–52.

[20] His dissertation was entitled *De barometri mutationibus*. There is a copy in the BWD library at Offenbach-am-Main.

[21] H. Hildebrandsson and L. Teisserenc de Bort, *Les bases de la météorologie dynamique.* 2 vol., Paris 1898, 1900; Vol. I, p. 45.

[22] H. W. Dove, 'Ueber den Zusammenhang der Hygrometeore mit den Veränderungen der Temperatur und des Barometers.' *Ann. der Phys.* 89 (1828), 305–27.

vapour contained in it.'[23] So if we are to discuss hydrometeors we must determine the ways in which the temperature can be lowered. According to the cause of cooling, he suggests four classes of hydrometeors:

1. *Cooling by radiation.* Dew, hoar frost, sometimes glare ice.
2. *Cooling by orographic ascent.* (He adduces examples.)
3. Conduction of heat to or from the surface.

   (a) Contact with a cool surface. Evening mists.

   (b) Sudden advection of warm air over a cool surface. (He gives as an example the precipitation accompanying a south-westerly storm [!], and also the snowfall near the edge of an icefield or at a cold coast.)

   (c) Lowering of temperature without change of wind direction.

   (d) Ascent of air over land. (Examples: daily thunderstorms in the tropics, hail, volcanic clouds.)

4. *Mixing of winds.* (Examples: tornadoes [!], thunderstorms turning into steady rain, sleet showers, 'April weather', steady snow-falls, cirrus, cirro-stratus.)

The 'mixing' rains, Dove says, are the most frequent, the others being important only in times of light wind; and the rains of the fourth class affect the barometer most. From his statistical investigations he states it as a clear rule that the barometer falls when it rains with an east wind, and rises when it rains with a west wind.

His classification is of course inadequate, especially in regard to the examples given under 3(b) and 4. It is interesting to see him trying to make statistical sense of rain and wind on the assumption that what we call frontal rains are the result either of mixing or of cooling by contact with the ground. It is made even more interesting when we find him stating in a footnote that 'south winds . . . flow upwards on the resisting colder air as on a mountain'.[24] It is astonishing that such a fruitful idea, set forth so clearly, should have needed nearly a century to become really useful to meteorologists.

[23] *Ibid.*, p. 307. By *precipitation* Dove means the formation of visible forms of water.
[24] *Ibid.*, p. 315, note. '*Südwinde . . . an der widerstehenden kälteren Luft wie an einem Berge hinauffliessen.*'

The idea that long-continued southerly rains are produced by cooling from the ground goes back to the eighteenth century, as we have seen in Chapter Five, and nothing had happened to shake it. Dove's examples of 'mixing' rain are much more surprising, especially 'April weather' – that is to say, showers. It would seem that he had a perfect place for such phenomena in 3(d).

A much more coherent and better-supported classification was produced in 1841 by Elias Loomis, whose interest in meteorology was synoptic rather than statistical.[25] Loomis postulated four causes of precipitation, much like those of Dove: I. Radiation. II. Warm air coming in contact with cold earth or water. III. Mixing of warm and cold currents. IV. The sudden transport of air into elevated regions. He differed from Dove in his assessment of their relative importance.

Radiation, he thought, can produce only dew. The second cause produces fogs, as on the Newfoundland Banks. The third might produce light rain but the fourth cause, the elevation of air, is by far the most important, and merits further classification, as follows: (1) flow up a mountain slope, (2), by a volcanic eruption, (3) by a whirlwind, and (4):

> When a hot and cold current, moving in opposite directions, meet, the colder, having the greatest specific gravity, will displace the warmer, which is thus suddenly lifted from the surface of the earth, is cooled, and a part of its vapour precipitated. This is a cause which may operate in any locality, and with almost any degree of energy. It is believed, therefore, to be, at least in this latitude, the most common cause of rain.[26]

4. STORMS, GREAT AND SMALL

The period between 1830 and 1850 saw an unexampled activity in the study of storms – tornadoes, tropical hurricanes, and the larger storms on land and at sea that were later called cyclones. As a result of all these studies there was a very great increase in the understanding of the winds of the world – of what Hildebrandsson and

[25] Loomis, *Trans. Amer. Philos. Soc.* 7 (1841), 125–63.   [26] *Ibid.*, p. 157.

De Bort called dynamic meteorology in the book already referred to. Readers interested in the question may be referred to it again; here I shall try to confine myself as far as possible to the attendant growth in the understanding of the way in which rain is produced in these storms.

The names associated with this study after 1830 are Espy, Loomis, Péclet, Reid, Redfield;[27] three Americans, a Frenchman, and an Englishman. I propose to add a second Frenchman who has been completely forgotten. After 1850 the initiative seems to have passed largely to the Europeans, and the whole question to have gone more into the realm of theory.

William C. Redfield, an American engineer, began thinking about tropical storms in the 1820s. For us his importance is that he established for the first time that such storms are really in the form of whirlwinds.[28] This in itself does not help us with the theory of rain, but it was essential that it should be known. Unfortunately he ascribed to centrifugal force the fall of the barometer on the approach of such a storm, noting that when water is stirred in a cylindrical vessel its surface becomes concave. Regrettably Dove later lent his authority to this unfruitful and indeed quite erroneous idea. However, such storms were definitely shown to be great whirlwinds, and if any further proof were needed, it was provided by Lt-Col William Reid, the Governor of Bermuda, who, with access to Admiralty records, published a large amount of convincing data.[29] But Reid was even less interested in the theory of rain than Redfield, and intended only to perform a service to mariners, an aim in which he undoubtedly succeeded.

At about this time James Pollard Espy came to prominence in this subject, which he pursued single-mindedly for the rest of his life; so devotedly, indeed, that he became the prisoner of his own theories. His first public statement on the subject, in a journal relatively unknown, was important in that it tried to use the properties

[27] And others, such as Piddington, only important in the matter of winds.

[28] Redfield, *Amer. J. Sci.* 20 (1831), 17–51. In the seventeenth century Varenius (*Geographia generalis*, Amsterdam, 1650) and Dampier, (*A Voyage around the World*, London, 1697) had speculated that these were revolving storms.

[29] Reid, *An attempt to develop the law of storms* [etc.] London, 1838.

of moist air to explain the ascent of masses of air and the formation of cloud and rain.[30]

Although he does not describe any laboratory experiments in this paper, it is clear from later papers that he had made experiments with simple apparatus in which he had found that dry air is cooled about twice as much as saturated air for a given change of pressure. He also knew that moist air is lighter than dry, so that a mass of moister air ought to start to rise in a dryer environment. Then,

> . . . if any cause exists in nature to produce an upward motion of air highly charged with vapour, and to continue that motion for some considerable time, the quantity of vapour so condensed would be very great, and a rain would be thus produced which would continue as long as very moist air continued to ascend.[31]

Now comes the essential idea:

> It might be supposed that the equilibrium would soon be restored, more especially if upon the condensation of the vapour, the air containing it is condensed also, as is generally believed.
>
> This latter, however, is not the fact; for I find by calculation that the quantity of latent caloric given out by the change of vapour to water or cloud, is sufficient to produce an expansion in the air six times greater than the contraction caused by the vapour turning to water. This calculation is founded on these three principles, which are all demonstrated by experiment. 1st. The latent and sensible heat of steam is a constant quantity, equal to 1,212 of Fahrenheit. 2nd. The capacity of atmospheric air is 250, that of water being 1,000. 3rd. The expansion of air by heat is 1-480th of the whole, for every degree of Fahrenheit above its bulk at 32°.
>
> It follows from these facts, that whenever vapour, in an ascending current of air, begins to condense into cloud, there is an expansion of the whole mass of air as far as the cloud extends, caused by the evolution of the latent caloric of the vapour. Moreover, this evolution of caloric prevents the air in ascending from becoming cold as rapidly as it would by expanding if it was dry air.[32]

[30] J. P. Espy, 'Theory of rain, hail, snow and the water spout, deduced from the latent caloric of vapour and the specific caloric of atmospheric air,' *Trans. Geological Soc. of Pennsylvania* 1 (1835), 342–6. *Cf.* J. E. McDonald, 'James Espy and the beginnings of cloud thermodynamics,' *Bull. Amer. Meteorol. Soc.* 44 (1963), 634–41.
[31] Espy (1835), p. 342.　　[32] *Ibid.*, pp. 342–3.

Espy never seems to give the details of these calculations. We do not know whether he had read Poisson; but at any rate he could not have derived this idea from Poisson. But let us go on. After quoting some more calculations, he continues:

> It follows then, from these principles, that the higher this air ascends, the more will the equilibrium be disturbed, and that the equilibrium cannot be restored while very moist air, at the surface of the earth, continues to flow towards the ascending column.
>
> For moist air in ascending will constantly have some of its vapour condensed and its latent caloric evolved; and thus its specific gravity diminished below that of the surrounding air. While this process is going on, the barometer will fall underneath the forming cloud, even before it begins to rain; for the air, as it expands in the region of the cloud, will spread outwards, and thus diminish the quantity of gravitating matter over the region below; and if the depression of the barometer is given, the velocity of the upward motion of the air may be calculated.[33]

He made immense claims for this process:

> In short, it is believed that all the phenomena of rains, hails, snows and water spouts, change of winds and depressions of the barometer follow as easy and natural corollaries from the theory here advanced, that *there is an expansion of the air containing transparent vapour when that vapour is condensed into water.*
>
> It is now more than three years since I formed this theory, and all the facts which I have been able to collect since, particularly with regard to water spouts and hail, have confirmed me in its correctness.[34]

The next year he published an expanded version of his theory in a more accessible place.[35] In this he gives his own highly idiosyncratic picture of tropical storms and tornadoes, holding them to be composed of radially convergent winds, the air escaping by rising up the middle. His calculations of the vertical velocities produced in this way – not at all clear – gave spectacular results, and must have raised serious doubts about his theory.

[33] *Ibid.*, p. 343–4.   [34] *Ibid.*, p. 344. The italics are Espy's.
[35] Espy, *Franklin Inst. J.* 17 (1836), 240–46; 309–16.

However, it attracted much favourable attention, and in 1837 we find him chairman of an *ad hoc* committee reporting to the United States Congress. It of course involved him in a collision with Redfield,[36], [37] who maintained that many storms are of the nature of whirlwinds, or vortices. In his first 1836 paper Espy had carelessly described his radial-inflow model as a 'vortex', using the word several times, and Redfield quite reasonably objected to this. He also politely accused Espy and his committee of adopting some of his generalizations without acknowledgment. I think there was mis-understanding between the two men, Espy thinking that Redfield wanted the whirlwind to produce a downward motion in its centre.

In 1840 Espy went across the Atlantic and read a paper about his theory to the British Association.[38] According to Espy, who later printed this paper in full,[39] there was a discussion, in which John Stevelly claimed that in 1834 he had used the idea of cold produced by rarefaction to explain the propagation of storms. An examination of Stevelly's paper,[40] however, is of little value in this respect; he thought that the fall of rain produces a sudden vacuum, into which air rushes.

Espy also sent a communication to the Academy of Sciences at Paris; this was referred to a *commission* composed of Arago, Pouillet, and Babinet, who reported in 1841,[41] at unusual length and most enthusiastically, ending with the hope that the government of the United States would put Espy in a position to pursue his important work. It is rather surprising that none of the three distinguished members of the *commission* questioned Espy's calculations; but at any rate the acceptance of their report by the Academy did nothing to impair his self-confidence.

In 1841 he published an extensive book on the subject,[42] many

[36] Espy, *Franklin Inst. J.* 18 (1836), 100–8.

[37] Redfield, *Franklin Inst. J.* 19 (1837), 112–27.

[38] B.A.A.S., Glasgow, 1840. *Rep. of Sections*, pp. 30–39.

[39] Espy, *Philosophy of storms.* Boston, 1841, 'Introduction', pp. vi–xxviii. The discussion, pp. xxviii–xxxi, does not appear in the B.A.A.S. report; nor is there any reference to one.

[40] Stevelly, B.A.A.S., Edinburgh, 1834, *Rep. of Sections*, pp. 564–6. Also summarized in *The Athenaeum* (1834), No. 361, pp. 713–14.

[41] *Compt. Rend.* 12 (1841), 454–62.   [42] Espy, *Philosophy of storms.* Boston, 1841

pages of which were devoted to the presentation of data which he believed to support his ideas of the structure of storms. By this time he had extended his theory to the larger travelling weather systems. In these, he interpreted the data to mean that air was converging not to a centre but to a line, this usually running in a direction from south-west to north-east and progressing across the country. This, as we can now see, was a clever and not too fanciful interpretation of the inadequate synoptic data then available.

But a much better interpretation was provided by Elias Loomis in the paper[43] referred to at the end of Section 3 of this chapter, and dated in the same year as Espy's book. Loomis, with great patience, had made use of all the meteorological observations he could lay his hands on, to study the great storm that passed across the north-eastern United States in the period 20 to 23 December 1836. He was impressed by the sudden fall of the barometer at each station, followed by a sudden rise, and by the very sudden fall of temperature and the shift of the wind to northerly that occurred when the barometer started to ascend. The fall of temperature was most impressive; at Augusta, Illinois, it amounted to 38°F. in the course of a morning. By a study of the wind patterns he was convinced that 'the conclusion is inevitable; the north-west wind displaces the south-east one by flowing under it ... The south-east current [makes] its escape by ascending from the surface of the earth.'[44] On page 159 he shows a cross-section through what would now be called a frontal surface.

Loomis, as the reader will see clearly if he will refer back to p. 154, emphasized the process of under-running, whereas Espy, with much less prescience, had neglected it. Espy's great contribution to meteorology was that he drew attention to one of the sources of the energy that drives storms, although vastly over-estimating the power of rising air. But he clung tenaciously to his first conclusions, and rapidly fell out of step with the progress of the science. In a popular biographical article written long after Espy's death, Cleveland Abbe gently pointed out what had been wrong:

[43] Loomis, *Trans. Amer. Philos. Soc.* 7 (1841), 125–63.
[44] *Ibid.*, p. 154–5.

Prof. Espy is charged with the one scientific defect that, with his deep conviction of the truth of his theory, and the enthusiasm it fed in him, he could not pass beyond a certain point in its development, and for the same reason his deductions were often unsafe. He was not prone to examine and re-examine premises and conclusions, but considered what had once been passed upon by his judgment as finally settled.[45]

We cannot leave Espy without mentioning his grandiose suggestion for rainmaking, a suggestion that could only have been made at the time when the great forests of North America were being cleared – or destroyed, according to one's point of view:

> Now, if masses of timber, to the amount of forty acres for every twenty miles, should be prepared and fired simultaneously every seven days in the summer, on the west of the United States, in a line of six or seven hundred miles long from north to south, then it appears highly probable from the theory, though not certain until the experiments are made, that a rain of great length, north and south, will commence on or near the line of fires; that the rain will travel towards the east side-foremost; that it will not break up until it reaches far into the Atlantic Ocean; that it will rain over the whole country east of the place of beginning; that it will rain only a few hours at any one place, . . . that it will rain enough and not too much at any one place; . . .[46]

and confer all sorts of benefits, which he enumerates, at a cost of $\frac{1}{2}$ cent per capita per annum! This holocaust was not approved by a Congress often resistant, in those days, even to relatively minor scientific expenditures; but as an expression of the American character the proposal deserves to be remembered. It would not, of course, have produced the widespread rains he predicted.

To return to Loomis, who in 1846 published a study of some further storms,[47] we find that he has recognized by this time that the energy released by the condensation of water vapour in the rising air will be a powerful addition to the effects of under-running, and that he understands that the vertical lapse rate of temperature is established by vertical interchange.

But before this, an interesting piece of theory, with wide

[45] C. Abbe, *Popular Science Monthly*, April 1889, p. 840.
[46] Espy, *Second and third Reports on Meteorology to the Secretary of the Navy*, U.S. Congress, 31st session (Senate), *Exec. Doc.* No. 39, 1850, p. 20.
[47] Loomis, *Trans. Amer. Phil. Soc.* 9 (1846), 161–84.

implications for the future, had been carried out in France by J. C. E. Péclet, a professor of physics,[48] who seems to have been the first to point out that the rate of cooling with change of pressure, calculated from Poisson's equation, is greater than that usually found in balloon ascents, so that the warm air of the lower layers cannot rise under these conditions, and even a mass of air at a high temperature can only rise to a certain height. He showed how to find this height, for a mass of air at any initial temperature, by plotting on a diagram with pressure as abscissae and temperature as ordinates, two curves – the curve representing the state of the atmosphere, and Poisson's curve for the sample of heated air. This air could not rise higher than the elevation corresponding to the pressure at which the two curves intersect. This was, as far as I know, the first use of an aerological diagram; but it was only valid for the unsaturated air to which Poisson's equation refers.

I now propose to go back to 1832, in which year the Paris Academy renewed a competition for a prize to be given for the best complete theory of hail. This had originally been announced in 1830, but none of the contestants had satisfied the Academy, which is not surprising in view of the very comprehensive requirements they set out. The second call produced, in due course, nine essays. Again nobody was given the prize – the Academy was asking the impossible – but entry no. 7 was reported on at some length in the official document[49] that closed the subject. This entry was sent in by P. H. Maille of St Florentin in the Department of the Yonne, and if it had been published, would have had the priority over every other attempt to apply Poisson's theory to the atmosphere, and in particular to study the ascent of moist air. It certainly did not fulfil the requirements for the prize, but if the *Commission*, composed of Arago, Becquerel, Gay-Lussac, and Dulong (as *rapporteur*) had acted less administratively and with more scientific acumen, this excellent effort would certainly have seen the light of day.

[48] Péclet, *Traité de physique*. Paris, 1843, Vol. I, pp. 576 ff. I have used the review in *Ann. der Phys.* 58 (1843), 655–60.

[49] Académie Royale des Sciences. *Séance publique du lundi 8 décembre 1834. Annonce des prix décernés par l'Académie des Sciences pour l'année 1834*, pp. 5–7.

Fortunately, through the helpful interest of Madame P. Gauja, the Secretary-Archivist of the *Académie*, Maille's original manuscript has been found in its Archives, together with a supplement. The main manuscript, received 28 February 1834, consists of forty-five leaves written on both sides; the supplement, twenty-one pages on eleven leaves, was received 30 September 1836, long after the contest was over. This is an instance of the disinterested attachment to science, evident throughout the work of Maille, who seems to have had little formal scientific training.

The manuscript is a remarkable document,[50] showing a clear understanding of the problems of meteorology as they existed at the time, as well as praiseworthy powers of self-criticism. Maille begins with a statement of the interdependence of meteorological pheno-mena and the difficulty engendered by the impossibility of conduct-ing full-scale experiments. He then sets up a model atmosphere in which a sample cubic metre of air, initially having a certain pressure, temperature, and humidity, rises because it is slightly warmer than its environment. Using Poisson's formula he follows it up to the satura-tion level; but above this level – and this is his original contribution – he takes into account the heat liberated by condensation, as well as the volume change due to the same cause, and finds that the rising saturated air cools off less rapidly than it would do if it were unsatura-ted. He frankly admits that he is unable to deal analytically with this problem, and solves it numerically, with a good deal of trial and error.

So far, as he is at pains to point out, he has neglected the effect of conduction from the surrounding air, mixing at the edges, and radiation. While he cannot deal with these entirely quantitatively, he shows that they cannot vitiate his main conclusions. Next he examines the amount of precipitated water in the whole column and shows that it is more than sufficient to explain heavy rainfall. He is, of course, embarrassed by a lack of knowledge of the vertical lapse-rate in the environment, and simply assumes that this is everywhere 2°C. cooler than his rising current, though nothing depends on the

---

[50] A more extended examination of Maille's work will be published elsewhere.

actual figure. No more than Espy did he realize that the height to which his sample of air could rise is strictly determined by the vertical distribution of temperature in the surrounding air.

Nevertheless there is no question that he would have had the priority over Espy if his paper had been published; nor that his thinking about the problem was more precise and more quantitative than that of Espy. His priority was recognized by Babinet in 1849,[51] but for some reason the Academy of Sciences would never publish his memoir, even in the greatly extended and improved form that he eventually gave to the world at his own expense in 1853.[52] This seems to have received no attention.

In any event, the development of the theory of rain had to proceed without Maille, and from this point it depended on the mathematical physicists.[53] The theory of convective equilibrium was worked out in 1862 by William Thomson (later Lord Kelvin), acting on a suggestion by Joule.[54] A more directly meteorological approach was taken by Théodor Reye, who made it clear that ascending moist air needs a different treatment, and emphasized the conclusions of Péclet regarding the necessity of studying the vertical distribution of moisture and temperature in the environment.[55] As a result of his work he was able to show that Espy's idea of the driving power of rising air had been altogether too optimistic, and indeed that for any driving-power to be produced at all, the vertical lapse-rate of temperature must exceed a certain amount.

But the most important paper of the 1860s on this subject – possibly the most important meteorological paper of the decade – was written by a mining engineer at Tarbes called H. Peslin.[56] It was unfortunately published in a journal where it would not be seen by

[51] Babinet, *Compt. Rend.* 28 (1849), 301–3.
[52] P. H. Maille, *Nouvelle théorie des hydrométéores* [etc.]. Paris, 1853.
[53] *Cf.* J. E. McDonald, 'Early developments in the theory of the saturated adiabatic process,' *Bull. Amer. Meteorol. Soc.* 44 (1963), 203–11.
[54] Thomson, *Proc. Manchester Lit. & Phil. Soc.* 2 (1862), 170–6; *Trans. Manchester Lit. & Phil. Soc.* 2 (1865), 125–31.
[55] Reye, *Zeits. für Math. und Phys.* 9 (1864), 250–76.
[56] Peslin, 'Sur les mouvements généraux de l'atmosphère.' *Bull. hebd. Assoc. Sci. de France* 3 (1868), 299–319.

the meteorologists, and Peslin has scarcely been mentioned in the history of the subject, unless merely in a parenthesis.[57]

Peslin begins his paper by calculating the adiabatic lapse-rate both for unsaturated air and for saturated air, and compares the results of his calculations with experimental values, finding remarkably good agreement. He then asks how it is that this effect seems to take precedence over the phenomena of solar and terrestrial radiation, winds and storms. This is not chance, he replies, but results from the fact that the values given by his formula mark the limits of stability of the atmosphere.

Consider an atmosphere in which the rate of decrease is more rapid than the appropriate limit. Then consider:

> an infinitely small mass of air, and let us impress on it a virtual displacement along the vertical. It will be cooled during its ascent, but according to our hypothesis the decrease of its temperature will be less than the difference of temperature between the layer from which it started and that in which it has arrived. Therefore the mass of air will be warmer after its displacement than the air in the layer of atmosphere which it has attained; so it will be lighter under the same pressure, and will tend to continue its ascent under the action of buoyancy alone, without the need for any new impulse.

> . . .

> These ascending currents, revealed to the eye by the formation and movements of cumulus, . . . may be compared to a thermal regulator; they arise at the points that are most rapidly heated, and arrest the increase of the temperature there; they bring warm air to the layers of the atmosphere that are still cold.[58]

The addition of all these effects tends to produce a constant rate of decrease of temperature with height. The energy is chiefly supplied to the lower layers because of the greater absorption of sunlight by water vapour in the atmosphere, and by the earth.

[57] As by J. von Hann, *Zeits. österr. Ges. Meteorol.* 9 (1874), 321. Even Schneider-Carius, in his excellent source book *Wetterkunde, Wetterforschung* (Freiburg & München, 1955, p. 259), mentions Peslin only in quoting this passage by von Hann.
[58] Peslin (1868), pp. 306–7.

Peslin then attempts a dynamical theory of storms, using a diagram after the manner of Péclet, but with height as abscissa and temperature as ordinate. It will not do to consider only the horizontal component of the movement of the air; admitting a rotary motion, he concludes that the energy to drive the storm comes from the latent heat of condensation, and that it will be greater, the greater the lapse-rate, and the more nearly the air is saturated. If the air becomes stable, the storm will quickly die out. Thus every revolving storm ought to give rain, for it is only when the air goes beyond its point of saturation that any motive power is developed. Peslin also shows that even a very heavy rain corresponds to the precipitation of less than half the water usually in the atmosphere in temperate latitudes. He supports his theory by quoting some large values of the lapse-rate observed in hailstorms, and by the observation that the storms in the North Atlantic often seem to follow the Gulf Stream, where the requisite conditions of temperature and moisture prevail.

The main conclusions of Peslin's very well thought out paper were supported by Reye in a book published in 1872, when he was a professor at Strasbourg.[59] Reye made an advance on Peslin in suggesting that the linear progress of revolving storms is due to the massive condensation on their leading sides; but in a review of the paper, J. von Hann[60] pointed out that this does not explain why they generally move eastwards and polewards, and not in some other direction.

In the following year Elias Loomis, as the result of the analysis of storm paths over a period of 314 days in 1872 and 1873, claimed that a cyclonic storm moves eastwards *because* there is more rainfall to the east of the centre.[61] The liberated latent heat expands the air, which rises and flows away in the upper regions, producing a lower

[59] Th. Reye, *Die Wirbelstürme, Tornados und Wettersäulen in der Erdatmosphäre mit Berucksichtigung der Stürme in der Sonnen-Atmosphäre*. Hannover, 1872. The reference to sunspots is in connection with a thoroughly wrong-headed theory of cyclones maintained for thirty years by H. Marie-Davy and H. Faye, both of whom had official positions of prominence in Paris. I have not space to consider this.
[60] *Zeits. österr. Ges. Meteorol.* 8 (1873), 111.
[61] Loomis, *Amer. J. Sci.* 8 (1874), 1–15.

pressure to the east. In this connection it should be mentioned that even in the fourth edition of H. W. Dove's *Das Gesetz der Stürme*[62] the great climatologist, though out of touch with the progress of dynamical meteorology, insisted that the ascending current of air could neither maintain nor steer a revolving storm, but he admitted that whirling winds have been seen over large fires.

In his 1874 paper already referred to,[63] von Hann gives an excellent summary of the theory up to that time. But then he demonstrates that even he – certainly one of the greatest of meteorologists – had not understood its full implications. Describing what we should now call a warm-front phenomenon, in which cirro-stratus is followed by strato-cumulus, he thinks that the resulting rain is produced in this way:

> ... the formation of the lower layer of stratocumulus proceeds imperceptibly from a sinking cirrostratus. In such a case the upper air-currents could nevertheless be so relatively cold that they could cool down the lower layers even when descending.[64]

This is in summer. In winter he can only assume that an upper warm current increases in strength and mixes with the colder air below at their boundary. In extenuation of von Hann's error it must be said that the phenomenon was not properly understood until after the first Great War.

The mention of cirro-stratus makes it opportune to go back to 1866 and two papers by E. Renou,[65] better known as a climatologist. He believed that for the full development of hydrometeors there are required two layers of cloud: cirriform clouds above, dropping ice crystals into the supercooled drops found in clouds at a lower level. This idea was several decades ahead of its time, and of course tacitly put numerous questions to which no answer was immediately forthcoming. But it did point out the possible rôle of water in a solid state, a consideration that led Heinrich Hertz to undertake an extension

[62] Berlin, 1873, p. 161–4.
[63] *Zeits. österr. Ges. Meteorol.* 9 (1874), 321–9; 337–46.   [64] *Ibid.*, p. 340.
[65] Renou, *Compt. Rend.* 62 (1866), 825–6; *Ann. Soc. météorol.* de la France 4 (1866), 89–106.

of the thermodynamics of the moist atmosphere.[66] Hertz pointed out that if a parcel of air rises far enough, it will pass successively through four conditions: (1) the *dry stage*, in which it is still unsaturated; (2) the *rain stage*, in which saturated vapour and liquid water are present; (3) the *hail stage*, in which saturated vapour, water, and ice coexist, and (4) the *snow stage*, where vapour and ice are together in the air.

In 1888 W. von Bezold, then professor of meteorology at Berlin, wrote the first[67] of a series of papers in which he made possible the convenient application of theory to the upper-air data that were just beginning to become available. It would be outside the scope of this book to follow the development of these methods further.

I shall end this section by a quotation from the first of a brilliant series of papers by Frank G. Bigelow of the United States Weather Bureau, which may give an indication of the way in which thermodynamic theory and synoptic and aerological observation were interacting in the first decade of the twentieth century:

> It has been shown conclusively for the United States that there are no true local warm-centered and cold-centered cyclones or anticyclones in the atmosphere, and that all the theoretical discussions of these founded on that basis are misdirected. The observations demonstrate that in the lower atmosphere the actual mechanism consists of rather deep warm and cold countercurrents of air, which underrun the prevailing eastward drift. The centers of gyration are uniformly in the region where these counter-flowing currents meet each other, that is to say, on the edges rather than in the midst of the warm and cold regions. About one half of the cyclone is relatively warm and the other half cold, while the opposite half of the anticyclone is warm and its alternate half is cold. Thus, in the United States, the eastern and northern sectors of the cyclone with the western and northern sectors of the anticyclone are warm, while the western and southern sectors of the cyclone and the eastern and southern sectors of the anticyclone are cold. The warm air flowing from the southwest into the east of the cyclone and west of the anticyclone, and the cold air flowing from the

[66] Hertz, *Meteorol. Zeits.* 1 (1884), 421–31. Hertz is remembered for his experimental proof of the existence of the electromagnetic waves known nowadays as microwaves.

[67] Von Bezold, *Sitzungsber. Preuss. Akad. Wiss.* (1888), 485–522; 1189–1205.

northwest into the east of the anticyclone and the west of the cyclone, constitute two currents whose temperatures differ from each other and from the normal temperature of the prevailing eastward drift. These currents seek to equalize their different temperatures by interpenetration, and in so doing the circulating structures known as cyclonic and anticyclonic are established. The heat added to the tropical zones of the earth by the solar radiation is to a considerable extent transported into the temperate zones by long horizontal currents in the lower levels, and is there expended in generating local circulations. These penetrate the upper current of eastward drift and tend to retard its motion, slowing it down to the moderate velocities which have been found to exist within ten miles of the ground. This stratification and interpenetration of currents of different temperatures is the true source of the energy of storms. The heat energy derived from the condensation of aqueous vapor by water, and the energy produced by purely dynamic eddies are entirely secondary in importance to the thermodynamic energy obtained by the counterflow and underflow of warm southerly currents against the cold northerly currents and beneath the eastward flowing drift.[68]

This was material for development between the two Great Wars.

5. THE GROWTH OF RAINDROPS

There are two obvious ways in which tiny droplets can grow until they become the raindrops which fall from the sky and splash on the pavement. Either they can collect water as they fall through the moist air, or they can grow by coalescence. Indeed they can do both; and the estimation of the relative contribution of the two processes is an important problem of cloud physics.

The reader may remember that in the eighteenth century it had been shown that when similar raingauges were placed at various elevations above ground, the apparent rainfall decreased as the height of the gauge increased.[69] The explanation almost universally adopted was that the drops were increasing in size by the condensation of vapour on them as they approached the ground. Doubts that this was the correct explanation gradually arose; for example H. Boase

[68] F. H. Bigelow, *U.S. Monthly Wea. Rev.*, Washington. 34 (1906), p. 9.
[69] See p. 98 above.

of Penzance noted in 1822 that the difference is, for some reason or another, proportional to the speed of the wind,[70] and, conjecturing that this was due to eddies, recommended a gauge sunk level with a large space of ground. But still almost everyone believed in the growth of drops.

There is not space here to go into this question in detail.[71] A very influential study was that made by W. Gray, Jr, and J. Phillips at York, and reported to the British Association in 1833–35.[72] Finding the variation in winter more striking than in summer, they assumed that the results were a function of the temperature, and dismissed in no uncertain terms the idea that the phenomenon is due to wind or to eddies. This was duly reported by J. C. Poggendorf in his *Annalen*, but he added a note with a calculation in it.[73] Making very liberal assumptions about vapour content, he showed that the results of Gray and Phillips could hardly occur if condensation were the only cause. In 1838 Professor A. D. Bache of Philadelphia, who by this time obviously disagreed with their conclusions, made a report.[74] He had put four similar gauges at the corners of the parapet of a square shot-tower 162 feet high and 12 feet square, and found ratios of as much as 2·32 to 1 in the rainfall, this between the SE and NW gauges in a strong westerly wind. When the gauges were elevated on poles 6 feet above the parapet, there was comparatively little difference between them.

This ingenious and, one would think, decisive experiment seems to have gone almost unnoticed. The eminent James D. Forbes of Edinburgh, in a formal report to the British Association on 1840, accepted Gray & Phillips's theory lock, stock, and barrel.[75] But evidence accumulated, and in 1861 W. S. Jevons was able to demonstrate conclusively the connexion with wind and to relate it to the

[70] Boase, *Annals of Philosophy*, n.s.4 (1822), 18–21.

[71] John C. Kurtyka, *Precipitation Measurement Study*; State of Illinois, Water Survey Division, Report of Investigation no. 20, Urbana, Ill., 1953, lists 77 references to the effect of the height of the gauge on the measurement of rainfall.

[72] *British Assoc. for the Adv. of Sci. Reports*: 1833, Trans. of Sect., 401–12; 1834, Trans, of Sect., 560–3; 1835, Report, 171–9.

[73] *Ann. der Phys.* 33 (1834), 222, note.

[74] Bache, *B.A.A.S., Newcastle, 1838*, Trans. of Sect., 25–27.

[75] Forbes, *B.A.A.S., Glasgow, 1840*, 112.

disturbed stream-lines of the wind passing an obstacle such as the gauge.[76]

The result of all this activity was to show that developed raindrops do not grow much in the last part of their course towards the ground; but what happens in the clouds? In the nineteenth century any information about this had to be obtained indirectly.

From the theoretical point of view an immensely important step was taken in 1870 by Thomson,[77] who showed that because of surface tension, the vapour pressure over a curved surface of liquid differs from that over a flat surface. For a droplet, the vapour pressure is greater than that over a flat surface by an amount proportional to the reciprocal of the radius of the droplet. The application of this to our problem is obvious. Suppose a cloud consisting of a large number of drops of different sizes. Then the vapour pressure at the surface of the smaller droplets will be greater than that over the larger ones, and water will therefore evaporate from the smaller droplets and condense on the larger.

Thus the growth of cloud droplets must to some extent proceed by the collection of vapour. But to what extent? The famous engineer Osborne Reynolds considered the question in 1877, and concluded that the process is too slow.[78] They must therefore grow by collecting other cloud particles, until the limit of their size is reached, beyond which they will be blown to pieces by the rush of air past them as they fall.

But up to the end of the nineteenth century very little was known of the actual sizes of raindrops, or their speed of fall. The latter was investigated at great length by P. Lenard in 1904.[79] Drops, he states, can be divided into three groups according to their diameters: (A) Small drops, whose terminal speed varies as the square of the radius.[80] (B) Larger drops, up to 1·1 mm in diameter, for which the speed varies as the square root of the radius, because of the

[76] Jevons, *Phil. Mag.* 22 (1861), 421–33.

[77] William Thomson, 'On the Equilibrium of Vapour at a Curved Surface of Liquid.' *Proc. Roy. Soc. Edinb.* 7 (1870), 63–68.

[78] Reynolds, *Proc. Manchester Lit. & Phil. Soc.* 16 (1877), 23–33.

[79] Lenard, *Meteorol. Zeits.* 21 (1904), 249–62.

[80] According to 'Stokes's law'. (See p. 59 above).

effect of turbulence. (C) Drops large enough to be deformed in falling, for which only an experimental treatment is possible. He says that he had observed this deformation in flash illumination in 1887; as a matter of fact G. Magnus had observed it in this manner in 1859.[81] Lenard made elaborate experiments, in which a drop of measured size was suspended in a vertical upward current of air. His most unexpected result was that drops with any diameter over 4·5 mm had a speed of about 8·0 m. sec^{-1}; this is less than twice as fast as a drop 1 mm in diameter falls.

Calculations show, says Lenard, that droplets ought to collide frequently if they differ in size – as they do; but nevertheless many clouds do not rain. It must be assumed that many collisions do not result in union, and Lenard thinks that this could be because of a layer of air absorbed on them, or perhaps because of electrical charges.

The measurement of the size-distribution of raindrops was undertaken in 1895 by Julius Wiesner,[82] in the tropics, and more extensively in Europe by A. Defant in 1905.[83] After testing the accuracy of Wiesner's method – catching raindrops on filter paper powdered with the dye eosin and measuring the resulting stains – Defant measured 10,017 raindrops, and found the weight of the drops to cluster about integral multiples of some small weight, especially the multiples 1, 2, 3, 4, 6, 8, 12, 16, etc., with the main maxima at 1, 2, 4, 8. This seemed to hold for individual rains, whether quiet and long-continued or violent and stormy.

This obviously supports the coalescence theory of the growth of raindrops, and Defant believed that distillation on to larger drops will proceed so slowly that most of the growth is by coalescence. His results suggested that drops of equal size coalesce more readily than unequal drops. This was explained by Wilhelm Schmidt in 1908[84] as being due to the hydrodynamical attraction produced when two drops are falling side by side at the same or nearly the

[81] Magnus, *Ann. der Phys.* 106 (1859), 21.
[82] Wiesner, *Akad. Wiss. Wien, Sitzungsber., Abt. 1,* 104 (1895), 1397–1434.
[83] Defant, *Akad. Wiss., Wien, Sitzungsber., Abt. 2A,* 114 (1905), 585–646.
[84] Schmidt, *Meteorol. Zeits.* 25 (1908), 496–500.

same speed. He showed that the available distances and times are more than adequate.

These researches provided a basis for a large part of the thriving field of research now known as 'cloud physics'. Improvements in technique and theory have gone on with an accelerated speed, especially since 1945.[85]

6. THE NUCLEI OF CONDENSATION

We must now go even farther back into the process by which invisible water vapour is converted into visible precipitation, and examine the comparatively recent history of the physics of the first stage of this process – the condensation of water vapour into the tiny particles of clouds and fogs.

For over two centuries after Guericke noticed the cloud in the receiver of his air pump, it had been taken for granted that this change of state occurs without any mediation whatever. As soon as it was known that air is cooled by its expansion,[86] it was firmly believed that water vapour condensed into cloud or fog as soon as the air containing it reached the dew point. No complications in this process were even suspected, until in 1875 some surprising experiments were reported in France by P. J. Coulier.[87]

Coulier was experimenting with the fog produced by the sudden expansion of air. His apparatus consisted of a glass flask with some water in it, connected by a tube to a hollow rubber ball. This was a completely closed system, and the pressure in the flask could be raised and lowered suddenly as often as desired without any introduction of fresh air into the system. Coulier found that when repeated experiments were made, fog did not continue to form indefinitely. This seemed to contradict the usual explanation. He also found that if the air were left standing in the flask for some days, or if the flask with the water in it were shaken for a few minutes, the air would

[85] The reader may be referred to B. J. Mason, *The Physics of clouds.* Oxford, the Clarendon Press, 1957.

[86] See p. 151 above.

[87] Coulier, 'Note sur une nouvelle propriété de l'air.' *J. de Pharmacie et de Chimie* 22 (1875), 165–73; 254–5.

not yield a fog on expansion; but if some of this now inactive air were replaced with air from the room the cloudiness could again be made to appear. Coulier, suspecting that something was coming in from the room besides atmospheric gases, tried filtering the room-air through a plug of cotton-wool. It became inactive, and he came to the conclusion that dust is necessary to the formation of a cloud in the flask. Realizing that this was important, he went to see the well-known physicist E. E. N. Mascart, who repeated the experiments and confirmed the results.

It is interesting that this was very nearly discovered in the eighteenth century by that virtuoso of experimentation, the Abbé Nollet,[88] while looking for the cause of the 'vapour' that appeared in the receiver of his air pump at the first strokes of the piston. He first assumed that it must be condensed moisture, coming from the ring of wet leather on which his bell-jar was resting; so he removed this and sealed the jar to the plate with soft wax. When he had done this he thought he had got rid of sources of moisture; but the 'vapour' still appeared when he operated the pump. So he concluded that:

> There is every reason to believe that this sort of vapour, the cause of which is being sought, is nothing else but the foreign bodies that are distributed in the air contained in the receiver.[89]

Note that Nollet thought that the fog was composed of the invisible foreign particles themselves, made visible by clumping together. He made numerous experiments, some very ingenious. He found less fog in his jar when the experiment was done in a clean room at the other side of the house than in his laboratory, where he had been distilling lavender and using various kinds of paint. He does not seem to have tried filtering the air. He did not realize, of course, that there was enough moisture in the air to make it possible, under the conditions in which he operated, for the fog to be composed of liquid drops.

To come back to Coulier, it is astonishing that his quite remarkable result had to be discovered all over again by John Aitken, who demonstrated it to the Royal Society of Edinburgh in 1881 in the

[88] Nollet, *Mém. Acad. Roy. Sci. Paris* (1740), 243–53.   [89] *Ibid.*, p. 244.

belief that it was entirely original.[90] It was only when his attention was drawn to Coulier's experiments by a letter in *Nature*[91] that he realized that he had been forestalled, as he freely acknowledged.[92]

Aitken carried the investigations much further than Coulier and Mascart had done. He observed that the fewer the particles, the coarser-grained the resulting fog, indicating that the available vapour was shared among the particles. And what is the dust made of? It must have many sources.

> Everything in nature which tends to break up matter into minute parts will contribute its share. In all probability the spray from the ocean, after it is dried and nothing but a fine salt-dust left, is perhaps one of the most important sources of cloud-producing dust. [There are also] meteoric dust, and volcanic dust, and condensed gases.[93]

Various substances contribute condensation nuclei when heated, but glass, metals, etc., which have been strongly heated will not (if kept clean) produce further nuclei at a lower temperature. The products of combustion, even those from a smokeless flame of dust-free gas burning in filtered air, contain very large numbers of particles on which fog will form under the right conditions.

> From this it will be observed that it is not the visible dust motes seen in the air that form the nuclei of fog and cloud particles . . . The fog and cloud nuclei are a much finer form of dust, are quite invisible, and though ever present in enormous quantities in our atmosphere, their effects are almost unobserved.[94]

Aitken wrote in a style not often found, even then, in scientific writing. I shall not resist the temptation to quote the conclusion of Part I of the paper in question:

> The ocean, which under a tropical sun quietly yields up its waters to be carried away by the passing air, almost looks as if he repented the gift, when tossed and angry under tempestuous winds, as he sends

---

[90] Aitken, *Trans. Rou. Soc. Edinb.* 30 (1881), 337–68. (*Collected works*, Cambridge, 1923, 34–64.)

[91] H. J. H. Groneman, *Nature* 23 (1881), 337.

[92] Aitken, *Nature* 23 (1881), 374–5. (*Collected works*, 65–67.)

[93] Aitken, *Trans. Roy. Soc. Edinb.* 30 (1881), 343.   [94] *Ibid.*, p. 350.

forth his spray, which dried and disguised as fine dust becomes his messenger to cause the waters to cease from their vapourous wanderings, descend in fertilizing showers, and again return to their liquid home.[95]

In further experiments he showed that various substances in a fine state of division differ enormously in their nucleating power. Many hygroscopic 'dusts' will form a 'dry fog' in unsaturated air, and Aitken takes this as another indication of the importance of dried sea-spray in meteorology.

We cannot follow all the further investigations made by this great experimenter on atmospheric nuclei.[96] By 1888 he was able to report to the Royal Society of Edinburgh that he could not only count the particles in a unit volume of air, but also count the number active at any given degree of supersaturation.[97] Because of the dependence of vapour pressure on the radius of a particle, more supersaturation is required for condensation on smaller particles. This work was done with a large laboratory apparatus. Aitken later made a portable apparatus, and finally a 'simple pocket dust-counter'[98] which served him and many other observers all over the world for many years.

I have not space to go into detail about Aitken's researches, but it is necessary to give some idea of his conclusions. The most fundamental of these is that water is deposited on many of the nuclei even in air that is not saturated. The resulting cloud of tiny droplets is what we know as haze. If the relative humidity increases, the particles take on more water and grow larger, so that the haze becomes denser. At just about the point of saturation a change takes place in the nature of the condensation; the abundant vapour condenses preferentially on the larger droplets, and a cloud, with optical properties different to the haze, quickly forms.[99] However, the hygroscopicity of the nuclei slows down the tendency of the larger droplets to grow at the expense of the smaller. This is because

[95] *Ibid.*, p. 355.   [96] The *Collected works* are a delight to read.
[97] Aitken, *Trans. Roy. Soc. Edinb.* 35 (1888), 1–19. (*Collected works*, 187–206.)
[98] Aitken, *Proc. Roy. Soc. Edinb.* 18 (1890–1), 39–52. (*Collected works*, 236–46.)
[99] See Aitken, *Proc. Roy. Soc. Edinb.* 17 (1889–90), 193–254. (*Collected works*, 297–331.)

175

as the smaller droplets evaporate, the concentration of the hygroscopic substances in them becomes larger, while that in the larger drops decreases as they increase in size.[100]

Given a slight degree of supersaturation, even non-hygroscopic nuclei can act, as was pointed out by Heinrich Mache.[101] At any given degree of supersaturation, drops of one particular radius will be in equilibrium with the ambient vapour pressure; but the required amount of supersaturation increases rapidly as the radius decreases, and as the supersaturation in the atmosphere is always very small, very small non-hygroscopic nuclei will never be active. Gaseous ions and small aggregates of water molecules will not act as nuclei in the free atmosphere.[102]

Information about the actual materials of the nuclei was hard to come by, but Aitken had no doubt that the two main classes were sea-salt and the products of combustion. This was agreed to by Albert Wigand, at least as far as the lower part of the atmosphere is concerned.[103] Wigand, who was much interested in the upper air, believed that dissolved gases must play a large part there, and quoted researches in support of this. He had also made experiments that showed him that the solid particles of real dust play little part in the process of condensation, as long as the dust is not hygroscopic. The Aitken apparatus, he rightly argued, should be called a nucleus-counter (*Kernzahler*), not a dust counter. But smoke contains very large numbers of nuclei, because of the hygroscopic products of combustion that accompany it.

[100] Aitken, *Trans. Roy. Soc. Edinb.* 37 (1892–3), 416–17.
[101] *Meteorol. Zeits.* 17 (1900), 554–7.
[102] Readers who are familiar with the cloud-chambers of physics laboratories must recollect that these operate with large degrees of supersaturation.
[103] A. Wigand, *Meteorol. Zeits.* 30 (1913), 10–18.

Chapter Nine

THEORIES OF DEW AND HOAR FROST

Of all the hydrometeors, dew has probably the fullest association with the more humane letters, with folklore, and – as the above quotation will suggest – with mythology. Moonlight nights are clear nights, which led the ancients to believe that the moon (*rorifera luna*) was the cause of the dew.

Aristotle was more sophisticated. In the *Meteorologica* he tells us that

> Any moisture evaporated during the day that does not rise far because the amount of the fire raising it compared to the amount of water that is being raised is small, falls again when it is chilled during the night and is called dew or hoar frost. It is hoar frost when the evaporation is frozen before it has condensed into water again . . . It is dew when the vapour has condensed into water . . . Both dew and hoar frost form in clear calm weather: no moisture will rise except in clear weather, and no condensation is possible in a wind.[1]

As we may suppose, few people ventured to disagree with this, which even to modern eyes is fairly good physics apart from one or two phrases; and for many centuries it was repeated over and over again. We shall jump to the year 1548, when Antoine Mizauld, an acute observer, amended Aristotle a little, and added cogent remarks

---

[1] Aristotle, *Meteorologica*, I, 10, translated by H. D. P. Lee (Loeb Classical Library, London and Cambridge, Mass., 1952), p. 73.

of his own,[2] as for example that the dew will not form under a tent. Aristotle had said that dew forms more easily in southerly winds than in northerly, 'which you will recognize', says Mizauld, 'not to be always true in the weather of this country [France]'.[3] More importantly, he makes a comparison between the formation of dew and the technical process of distillation; dew may be formed

> by the turning and revolution of vapour itself, making contact with some cold and massive body, as we see it happen in the heads of stills, and when pots are boiling on the fire; for when the vapour is thrown against the covers of these, if they are at all cold, it thickens and is converted into the substance of water.[4]

And frost, even slight, may change into hoar frost and fog (*frimas & brouillat*) matter that would otherwise form dew.

Thus by the seventeenth century it was quite clear that dew was the result of the condensation of vapour; but two problems remained: (1) did the vapour come from the earth or from the air, or in more common parlance, did dew 'rise' or 'fall'? (2) What was the source of the cold necessary for the condensation of the vapour? The second question sharpened into a discussion of cause and effect: did the cold produce the dew, or the other way round? These questions were not completely answered until late in the nineteenth century.

That there could be two answers to the first question was obvious at least as early as 1687, to judge by a discussion at the Académie Royale des Sciences in that year, where

> some said that dew comes from the earth and does not fall from above, because in bell-glasses[5] we see as much dew as in other places exposed to the air. Others believed that dew indeed comes from the earth, but rises to a certain height and falls down again, since those who go walking in the evening or early in the morning have their hair wet with dew. During the day these humid particles are agitated and sustain themselves in the air, but during the night they thicken and thus become heavier.[6]

[2] Antoine Mizauld, *Le Mirouer de l'air, autrement dict meteorologie, ou bien petit commentaire des choses de l'air.* Paris, 1548, pp. 22–24.

[3] *Ibid.*, p. 23.   [4] *Ibid.*, p. 24.   [5] *Cloches de verre*, used in horticulture.

[6] *Histoire de l'Académie Royale des Sciences depuis son établissement en 1666 jusqu'à 1699.* 11 vol., Paris, 1733; Vol. II, p. 21.

Here you have two distinct phenomena, and in the eighteenth century nearly all the important writers on the subject allowed that dew could either 'rise' or 'fall'; but of course the development of the subject could not outstrip the growth of knowledge of the nature and properties of water vapour itself.

One of the first serious experimenters was Christian Ludwig Garsten, whose treatment of dew seems to be much the best part of his book on meteorology.[7] Garsten came to the conclusion that dew really rises from the earth. He noted that when a brass plate was laid on the ground or suspended near it by threads, the lower surface was bedewed; but if it was suspended at a height of five feet, both surfaces were covered with dew. Substances like hay, straw, and wool were bedewed on the upper side as well as that nearest the ground.

Much more elaborate experiments were reported by C. F. du Cisternay du Fay, whose untimely death in 1739 deprived electrical science of one of its cleverest investigators. In a full-dress paper on dew,[8] Du Fay concluded that it rises from the earth. In general there was more dew collected on surfaces nearer the ground, and nearly always more dew on the underside of horizontal plates. In these experiments he followed the lead of Petrus Van Musschenbroek, who kept him in touch with similar work at Utrecht. On 27 August 1735, Musschenbroek had written to him about some experiments in which similar surfaces of various colours were exposed, collecting various amounts of dew. Du Fay at once had several bowls painted, and one left unpainted; this last received most dew, the yellow and white ones the least. He also found that glass, porcelain, and vitreous substances in general collected a good deal of dew, while polished metal collected almost none. Observations of this sort, as may be supposed, complicated the problem immensely.

Musschenbroek's observations were published in his influential

---

[7] *Christiani Ludov. Garsten tentamina systematis novi ad mutationes barometri ex natura elateris aërei demonstrandas* [etc.]. Frankfurt, 1733. I have used the long review in *Phil. Trans.* 38 (1733), 43–54.

[8] Du Fay, *Mém. Acad. Roy. Sci. Paris* (1736), 352–74.

textbook of physics, to which I have referred before.[9] His long article on dew,[10] dealing as it does with his own work, is one of the better parts of the book. The reason why dew collects more copiously on some kinds of surface than on others is, he confesses, beyond him, but he does himself credit by rejecting such hypotheses as electricity and chemical attraction. The dew on plants he believed to be an excretion of the plants themselves, different to dew on other objects. He believed that much dew rises, but also that some of it falls – at least at Utrecht, he admitted with his habitual caution – quoting several experiments in support of this. How, then does it wet surfaces oriented in any direction?

> Indeed, when we say that dew falls, we do not claim that it falls as quickly as rain, but only extremely slowly, like a very thin fog that falls softly from the air in which it is suspended. If then the particles are attracted by some object, either laterally, or from above, or from below, they will not fail to move towards it . . . In this regard it is like a full bottle of wine that is carried from a cold cellar into a hot and humid atmosphere, for this at once becomes moist on all sides, because the heat adhering to the particles of moisture (*le feu, qui tient aux parties humides*) tries to get into the cold bottle from all directions, and in consequence abandons the humidity, which is then left on the external surfaces of the bottle.[11]

This last passage is an excellent account of the relation between heat and water vapour as it was seen at the time. What we must not fail to notice is that the behaviour of the bottle of wine is only a simile, or a model for the behaviour of the dew. The next step was to see the two phenomena as identical.

The identification was made by Charles Le Roy of Montpellier, to whose important paper[12] I referred at some length in Chapter two.[13] Le Roy made many observations with his condensation hygrometer, and concluded that dew comes from the air. Except for changes of

[9] P. Van Musschenbroek, *Beginselen der natuurkunde* [etc.], Leiden, 1736. Trans. by Pierre Massuet as *Essai de physique*, Leyden, 1739, 2 vol. paged as one. I have used this translation.

[10] *Essai*, pp. 753–85.   [11] *Essai*, p. 766.

[12] *Mém. Acad. Roy. Sci. Paris* (1751), 481–518.

[13] Page 30 above. The reader may wish to refresh his memory by re-reading the passage.

wind, there was always dew at the Observatory of Montpellier when the temperature fell below the dew point (*degré de saturation*) during the night. As a standard body for observing dew, he used a bottle made of white glass. He noticed that there was seldom dew in the centre of town; this, he said, was because the temperature does not fall as low there as in the country.

Dew, said Le Roy, forms everywhere in the atmosphere near the ground, and attaches itself to the nearest surface, and so both the upper and lower surfaces are wetted. But the surface must not repel the dew, a property he assigns to polished metals.

Besides this aerial dew, there are two other kinds: the 'thick vapour, like a fog' that rises a few feet over damp meadows during the night, and the dew that forms on plants when there is none on more solid objects. These are to be ascribed mainly to vapour rising from the earth. The air does not cool at night as much as the leaves of the plants do. Because the leaves are cool, the vapour coming from the earth is intercepted by them on its way up. Le Roy disposes of Musschenbroek's idea that such dew is exuded from the plants by observing that a thin sheet of glass is bedewed under similar conditions. He objects to Du Fay's interpretation of his experiments with horizontal plates, suggesting that his plate near the ground would have received dew from the ground long before the upper plate took it from the air.[14]

At about the same time G. W. Richmann was working at Petersburg on evaporation.[15] By means of various experiments, he found that whether water colder than the ambient air lost or gained in weight depended on the temperature difference (it would presumably depend also on the humidity of the air), and was clever enough to suspect that this may have a relation to the occurrence of dew, and to the question whether it 'falls' or 'rises'. He thought that if the air is heavy with vapour, it may do both. More importantly, he realized that a temperature-inversion builds up at night:

[14] In the Yale University Library, Deluc MS., there are some unpublished observations on dew by J. A. Deluc, dated 1749, and somewhat like those of Le Roy. It may be supposed that the appearance of Le Roy's paper distracted Deluc from the subject.

[15] Richmann, *Novi Comment. Acad. Petrop.* 2 (1751), 145–61.

If it happens that there is a great difference between the temperature of the warmer air above and that of the lower air near the surface of the earth and of bodies located close to the ground, and if the surface of these is great in relation to the amount of material in them, they will attract the vapours strongly and there ought to be a greater collection of vapours on their surfaces, especially if those vapours rising from the ground are added . . . Hence if the collection of vapours observed in the morning is greater, either there is a greater difference in temperature between the warmer upper air and the colder lower air, or the air is more full of vapours, or both.[16]

Whatever may have been happening to the surface air, Richmann, in the language of parlour games, was getting warmer. But as it is the duty of the historian to pay some attention to the ideas that later proved unsuccessful as well as to the fruitful ones, I shall interrupt the narrative to mention two ineffective approaches to the phenomenon.

The first concerns hoar-frost.[17] The author of the paper in question had observed this when the thermometer (presumably at some distance above ground) was above freezing. He had also noticed the similarity between frost figures on a window and salt crystals in an evaporating pan. So he went back to an old theory of freezing – one that had been discredited by Boyle – which demanded 'frigorific particles' of some unidentified salt. 'It seems to me,' he said, 'that this very old theory of freezing is really quite sufficient to explain all the phenomena, so that there is no need of electricity or any other novelty.'[18]

The purveyors of novelties were not idle, and we find Franz Carl Achard of Berlin writing an article with a title that begins, ominously, 'Sur l'imperfection de la météorologie.'[19] He has observed that the occurrence of dew is preceded by a strong 'electric atmosphere' during the previous day. It also appears that dew is deposited more copiously on 'electrics' (non-conductors) than on 'non-electrics' (conductors); and he concludes that electricity is 'if not always, at least very often the cause of dew'.[20]

[16] *Ibid.*, p. 160.   [17] Wolf [Wolff?], *Phil. Trans.* 52, Part 2 (1762), 547–54.
[18] *Ibid.*, p. 554.   [19] *Mém. Acad. Berlin.* (1780), 14–23.   [20] *Ibid.*, p. 17.

Let us return to the main road. Deluc knew that clouds inhibit the formation of dew, and also reduce the nocturnal cooling. The reason seemed to him to be

> that when there are no clouds in the air at sun-set, or when they are dispersed, the heat of the inferior air, and that which rises from the earth, dissipates itself into the superior regions, and then the vapours which are dispersed throughout the air *condense and fall down again in dew;* but when the clouds are continued, and thus separate the inferior from the superior air, they prevent this dissipation of the heat, and the vapours remain suspended.[21]

The phrase that I have italicized seems a little out-of-date for 1773. As to how the heat is dissipated, the application of the radiation of heat from bodies at ordinary temperatures, destined to be very useful to meteorology, was some decades off.

The next important researches were carried out by Patrick Wilson, an astronomer at the Macfarlane Observatory near Glasgow. These concerned hoar frost. Patrick Wilson probably became interested in this matter through the work of his father, Alexander Wilson, who had experimented on the evaporation of ice in the cold winter of 1767–8.[22] The winter of 1779–80 was also very cold.[23] Patrick Wilson obtained a number of comparable thermometers and measured temperatures on the snow, in the air 30 inches above it, near a deposit of hoar frost, and so on. One night the thermometer on the snow read 14°F. lower than the one in the air. In view of his father's results he was tempted to ascribe this to evaporation from the snow, and devised a beautifully simple experiment to test this hypothesis. He got a bellows and let it cool, then blew on the thermometer lying on the snow; but instead of falling farther, it rose nearly to the air temperature. The experiment was later varied by fanning the thermometer with a sheet of brown paper fitted to the end of a long slender stick, with similar results. Finally he took a thermometer that had hoar-frost all over its bulb, and swung it

[21] J. A. Deluc, *Phil. Trans.* 63 (1773), 454. Italics added.
[22] A. Wilson, *Phil. Trans.* 61 (1771), 326–31.
[23] P. Wilson, *Phil. Trans.* 70 (1780), 451–73.

round on the end of a string. The mercury rose 2°F. It was clear that evaporation could not be the cause of the cold.

It is difficult for us who are used to the idea of nocturnal radiation to realize the depth of the mystery presented by these observations. Wilson did not know what to make of it, as he freely confessed:

> These experiments indeed rather favour the opinion of the excess of cold . . . depending upon a principle the very reverse of evaporation. But . . . it [is] too early to say anything decisive concerning the nature or extent of a cooling process which has so recently come under observation.[24]

He did conclude, rather tentatively, 'that very cold air is never disposed to deposit its contents except upon bodies as cold or colder than itself'. Exactly the same conclusion was expressed, but with more assurance, by Karl Ludwig Gronau,[25] a Berlin pastor who has the almost unbelievable distinction, according to Hellmann, of having made regular meteorological observations from 1756 until the year of his death – seventy years!

The next winter, Patrick Wilson continued his experiments, with the same results; he also felt that he had shown that the cooling was not due to any chemical reaction.[26]

The Wilsons had only observed in the presence of frost or snow, and in 1788 James Six, the inventor of a combined maximum and minimum thermometer, reported its use in establishing vertical temperature gradients up to a height of 220 feet – he used the tower of Canterbury Cathedral.[27] Six found that it was usually colder near the ground at night, warmer in the daytime, and the clearer the weather, the greater the differences of temperature. In spite of Wilson, not to mention Le Roy, he thought that

> This remarkable diminution of heat near the surface of the earth in clear weather, after the sun is set, and in the night, proceeds, I apprehend, partly from the coolness which the dews or vapours possibly may acquire in their descent, and partly from the evaporation which

[24] *Ibid.*, p. 469.   [25] Gronau, *Schrift. naturf. Freunde Berlin* 7 (1787), 343.
[26] P. Wilson, *Phil. Trans.* 71 (1781), 386–94.
[27] Six, *Phil. Trans.* 78 (1788), 103–20.

takes place at the same time from all moist or frozen bodies exposed to the open air, particularly from those on which dew or hoar frost is deposited.[28]

Six relegated these speculations to a footnote, as though they did not matter very much; but they raise the acute question whether the dew causes the cold, or vice versa. There is little doubt that contemporary opinion strongly favoured the first alternative.

Meanwhile Patrick Wilson finished demolishing the hypothesis that the cold was due to evaporation, by making weighings of a large pan containing snow, and finding that its weight increased by the accumulation of hoar-frost while the sky was clear, but decreased when the sky was clouded, at which time the temperature of the snow surface was about the same as that of the air.[29] He also compared the temperatures of snow, sand, and mercury, finding that dry sand got even cooler than snow, while mercury became little cooler than the air, and attracted little hoar-frost.

Wilson, entirely at sea, proposed no less than five hypotheses about the source of the cold: two chemical, two physical, and one – after reading Achard's paper[30] – electrical. He concluded only that the production of hoar-frost is accompanied by cold, whatever the nature of the surface, but that some substances 'attract' the hoar-frost at a greater rate. The disposition of the air to part with hoar-frost depends on a clear sky.

Never can a natural phenomenon have been more utterly in need of an organizing hypothesis. Yet by this time the materials for an explanation were at hand in the discovery of invisible radiant heat, the existence of which had been suspected for more than a century, but was not established beyond doubt until about 1774.[31] One of the most resourceful experimenters on the subject was Marc Auguste Pictet, a professor at Geneva, who showed not only that invisible heat was reflected and concentrated by paraboloidal mirrors, but also, by putting a flask full of snow at the focus of one mirror and

[28] *Ibid.*, p. 108, note.   [29] P. Wilson, *Trans. Roy. Soc. Edinb.* I (1788), 146–77.
[30] Referred to on p. 182 above.
[31] For a convenient summary see A. Wolf, *A history of science, technology, and philosophy in the 18th century.* 2 vols., London & New York, 1938, 2nd ed. 1952. Reprinted by Harper & Brothers, New York, 1961; Vol. I, pp. 206–12.

the bulb of a thermometer at another, that 'cold' could be radiated.[32]
To explain this last experiment, which was puzzling, Pierre Prevost,
also from Geneva, produced a theory of the equilibrium of radiant
heat by exchanges going on all the time between the bodies in a
system.[33] It was not that cold was radiated to the thermometer, but
that the thermometer radiated heat to the cold flask.

This excellent synthesis was accepted by Pictet. Meanwhile the
latter had made systematic observations on the vertical temperature
gradient up to a height of 75 feet, but, in spite of all he knew about
radiant heat, he explained the nocturnal inversion of the gradient
by reference to evaporation from the soil![34]

At this point in the story the subject fell into utter confusion.
There was not even agreement on whether dew 'fell' or was condensed out of the air. In the United States Noah Webster, the
famous lexicographer, made ingenious experiments in 1791[35] which
supported the idea of immediate condensation. John Dalton also
believed in this.[36] But on the other hand Luke Howard poured
scorn on the idea in the off-hand manner that he sometimes adopted:

> That the ordinary production of dew is by a real *descent* of water from
> the atmosphere, and not by decomposition of vapour on surfaces
> previously cooled, . . . any one may readily be convinced by observing
> in what abundance it is collected by substances which are wholly
> unfit to carry off the requisite quantity of caloric for the latter effect.[37]

[32] Pictet, *Essais de physique*. Geneva, 1790. The expriment seems to have been made
by Giovanni Antonio Magini, who died in 1617; for Sir Christopher Heydon (*An
astrological discourse* [etc.], London, 1650, p. 21), who also reports having made it,
adduces 'the testimonies of Maginus, who, in the representations of his [burning]
glass sent to the Emperor [Rudolph?], doth confirm the same in these words: *Species
esse sensu tactus perceptibilis, ut apparet ex lumine candelae, item ex nive & glacie infrigi-
dante per suam imaginem remotè admodum.*' I have not been able to find this passage, but
it must date from before 1611, the gift to the Emperor being mentioned in that year
in Magini's *Breve instruttione sopra l'apparenze et mirabili effetti dello specchio concavo
sferico.* Bologna, 1611, p. 4. The experiment was made again about 1660 by the
Accademia del Cimento (*Saggi di naturali esperienze* [etc.]. Third Florentine ed., Florence,
Tipografia Galileiana, 1841, pp. 114–15), who did not know what to make of it.

[33] P. Prevost, *Obs. sur la phys.* 38 (1791), 314–23.

[34] Pictet, *Essais*, pp. 171–82.

[35] Only published in 1809 in *Mem. Amer. Acad. Arts & Sci.* 3, part I, pp. 95–103.

[36] Dalton, *Meteorological observations and essays* (1793), 2nd ed. 1834, pp. 136–37.

[37] Howard, *Phil. Mag.* 16 (1803), 352.

If even this fundamental point was in question, how could anyone be expected to understand the very different behaviour of glass and of polished metal? Elaborate experiments were made, as for instance by another Prevost, this time from Montauban in the south of France.[38] The following is an example: A disk of metal was stuck to one side of a larger sheet of glass. Sometimes dew was deposited on the metal as well as on the glass, but more often not, in which case 'the preservative property' of the metal often extended to a considerable distance all round it. Moreover, if the metal is on top and dew has been deposited below, there may be a dry space opposite the metal disk. But the metal does not act as a shield (*abri*); for if gilt papers are applied to the glass, some with the gilt side outwards and some with the paper side outwards, only the former 'protect' the glass from the dew. Prevost's observations, as it seemed to him, established an important point: 'glass exercises its attraction for humidity . . . right through metals'.[39]

The real key to the mystery was provided almost immediately by the classical paper of Rumford on radiation from bodies with various surface properties.[40] Rumford found that polished metals radiate much less heat than other substances at the same temperature, and that glass is a very good radiator. (We now know that snow also radiates very strongly.) Strangely enough, Rumford was not willing to accept P. Prevost's theory of radiative equilibrium, and persisted in thinking that cold bodies have a radiation proceeding from them which has the power of 'generating' cold in warmer bodies.

The greater loss of heat from some surfaces than others was generally accepted, but the idea of invisible radiation found more mental resistance. John Leslie, for example, explained the difference by supposing

> that air never comes into actual contact with any surface, but approaches much nearer to glass or paper than to polished metal, from

[38] Benedict Prevost, *Ann. de Chim.* 44 (1803), 75–90.
[39] *Ibid.*, p. 89.
[40] Benjamin Thompson, Count of Rumford, *Phil. Trans.* 94 (1804), 77–182.

which it is separated by an interval of at least the 500th part of an inch.[41]

But by this time a synthesis was at hand. It was made by Dr William Charles Wells, who was born in 1757 at Charleston, South Carolina, but left America at the Revolution and finally settled in London, where he practised medicine. In 1812 he began to study dew with great patience, although he was in a state of health not very compatible with night experiments, and in August 1814, published his *Essay on dew*,[42] called by the famous physicist John Tyndall 'a model of wise enquiry and lucid exposition'.[43]

Wells was aware of much of the previous work, in particular that of Patrick Wilson and of James Six. But, he says early in the book, he has become convinced that their explanations of dew and hoar-frost are incorrect. He first thought that dew caused the observed cold, but later he realized that the cold had to be produced before dew could be deposited.

In his quantitative experiments he used weighed samples of wool. Apart from this, he repeated many experiments of other workers, but added crucial ones of his own. For example, he placed on a plot of grass, upright,

> a hollow cylinder of baked clay, the height of which was 2½ feet, and diameter 1 foot. On the grass, surrounded by the cylinder, were laid 10 grains of wool, which in this situation, as there was not the least wind, would have received as much rain as a like quantity of wool fully exposed to the sky. But the quantity of moisture obtained by the wool surrounded by the cylinder was only a little more than 2 grains, while that acquired by 10 grains of fully exposed wool was 16.[44]

[41] Leslie, *A short account of experiments and instruments, depending on the relations of air to heat and moisture*. Edinburgh, 1813, p. 20. The reader may be acquiring the impression that I am being hard on Leslie; but it cannot be denied that all his judgments about the matters we have been discussing were signally unfortunate.

[42] W. C. Wells, *An essay on dew and several appearances connected with it*. London, 1814. 2nd ed. 1815; 3rd ed. 1818; 4th ed. 1821. Reprinted with annotations by L. P. Casella and an appendix by R. Strachan, London, 1866. It is this reprint that I have used.

[43] Quoted by L. P. Casella in the preface to the 1866 reprint, p. iv.

[44] Wells, *Essay*, 1866 reprint, p. 15.

From this and many other ingenious experiments he concluded that 'whatever diminishes the view of the sky, as seen from the exposed body, occasions the quantity of dew which is formed upon it to be less than would have occurred if the exposure to the sky had been complete'.[45] And at the same time he felt that he had proved that it will not do to say that dew 'falls'.

When thermometers were placed in various places, those where most dew was formed were always found to read lowest. On cloudy nights grass was little or not at all colder than the air, but a sudden clearing rapidly lowered its temperature.

It would take too much space to follow all Wells's ingenious experiments, but his conclusions can be stated. The cooling of the earth's surface, and of the bodies that accumulate dew, is the result of radiation to space. This radiation is always going on, but can be largely interrupted by clouds; and in the daytime it is overbalanced by the radiation to the earth from the sun. Wells had an extremely clear view of what is now called the radiation balance of the atmosphere.

In conjunction with the work of Prevost, Rumford and Leslie, which Wells mentions, the hypothesis of radiation of course provides an adequate explanation for the small amount of dew on polished metals, the greater amount on finely divided substances, and so on.

Wells devoted several pages of his book to an examination of the idea that dew 'rises', *i.e.* that the vapour producing it is that emitted by the earth and plants; discussing especially Du Fay's finding that dew appears earlier on objects near the ground. He objects (1) that the air near the ground is colder, (2) that it is less liable to agitation, (3) that it often contains more moisture, including that which has risen from the earth. He also notes that dew, even heavy dew, can form where the ground is very dry, as in Egypt. But he does not deny that vapour escaping from the ground can add to the amount of dew, especially on grass.

He then disagrees with the opinion that the dew formed on plants is transpired from the plants themselves, arguing that it forms

[45] *Ibid.*, p. 14.

189

equally well upon dead vegetation; that it is not found on cloudy nights; and that in the cold and dark plants do not transpire very much. He concludes 'that almost the whole of the dew, which will afterwards form on the plant, must be derived from the air.'[46]

Wells really seems to have wrapped the matter up, except for the minority of people who could not believe in nocturnal radiation. One such doubter was Georg Wilhelm Muncke, one of the editors of the second edition of J. S. T. Gehler's *Physikalisches Wörterbuch*. In the extensive article on dew,[47] probably written about 1835, Muncke sets out to demolish Wells's theory, and indeed on p. 699 calls nocturnal radiation 'purely hypothetical'. His difficulty, which must have been shared by many people, seems to be the lack of a material body overhead for the earth to radiate to; if there were a mass of ice, he says, he could understand it; but there is nothing. Muncke adduces against nocturnal radiation the existence of 'frost hollows', low places where frost is more prevalent than on neighbouring higher ground. (Their real explanation is the drainage of the heavier, colder air.) As to how the objects on which dew is deposited are cooled, Munke is not clear; he seems to think the heat can just disappear (*verschwinden*).

But further evidence accumulated. In 1847 James Glaisher, one of the most prominent of nineteenth-century meteorologists, filled ninety-seven pages of the *Philosophical Transactions* with a paper on nocturnal radiation, including large tables.[48] His contribution to the problem of dew was to measure not only temperature but humidity, with the result that

> The formation of dew was found to depend solely on the temperature of the bodies upon which it was deposited, and it never appeared upon them till their temperatures had descended below that of the dew-point in their locality, as found by observations of a dry and wet bulb thermometer [sic!] placed in their vicinity.[49]

In the same year the Italian physicist Macedonio Melloni, who, having been the first to use the thermopile to measure radiation, had

[46] *Ibid.*, p. 96.
[47] *Gehler's phys. Wörterbuch*, n. ed., vol. IX part I, Leipzig, 1838, pp. 686–708.
[48] Glaisher, *Phil. Trans.* 137 (1847), 120–216.   [49] *Ibid.*, p. 126.

a sort of vested interest in the subject, wrote several letters to Arago, defending Wells's theory. These were published in the *Comptes Rendus* of the Paris Academy.[50] Melloni begins by saying that the violent attacks on the theory showed 'blind hostility', and prompted him to take the matter up. To avoid complications, he put thermometers in boxes of bright metal and others in similar boxes covered with soot, and demonstrated an enormous difference in emissivity. Then after a short historical account, he described his decisive experiment. A large tin disk was painted, out to a third of its radius from the centre, on one side only, the remainder being left bright. A smaller bright tin disk, of radius 5 mm less than that of the painted patch on the large disk, was cut, and both disks suspended 5 mm apart on a wire, and hung horizontally, the smaller disk above. Dew formed first on the annulus of paint projecting from under the small disk, and spread both ways, but chiefly outwards, because as soon as dew had formed on the metal cooled by conduction from the band of paint, this bedewed metal started to radiate strongly. A large space in the centre of the varnish remained dry, protected by the upper plate.

> But what one might perhaps not have predicted *a priori* is the exact reproduction of these phenomena on the [polished] lower surface of the large disk, turned towards the soil. The dew begins by showing itself, on that surface, in the parts opposite the little annular outer band of paint, and a faint whitish circle is perceived which, suddenly appearing on the dark background of polished metal,[51] recalls the formation of images in the Daguerrotype. This circle then becomes stronger and dilates little by little. It sometimes arrives at the edge, and never reaches the central part, which continues to keep its dryness and its metallic polish.[52]

This simple and beautifully ingenious experiment completely disposed of the idea that polished metals 'repel' dew, because it showed dew being deposited on one part of a surface of metal, and not on an adjacent one in the same plane. It also disposed of the idea that dew is formed in droplets that 'fall' or 'rise'. Combined

[50] Melloni, *Compt. Rend.* 24 (1847), 531–7, 641–6; 25 (1847), 499–501.
[51] No doubt reflecting the dark soil.
[52] *Compt. Rend.* 24 (1847), 536.

with the experiments with the thermometers it showed, Melloni believed, that dew is 'a pure consequence of nocturnal radiation'.

At least in Great Britain, Wells's theory of dew became an article of faith among physicists and meteorologists, the more so because of the beautifully clear and elegant way in which the book had been written. It took some courage, therefore, for John Aitken to maintain that Wells had been in error in grossly underestimating the contribution of vapour from the ground, and in denying that some dew on growing plants is in fact transpired water.[53]

Aitken's paper is most convincing. As a result of experiments (1) in which he found that under the conditions in which dew is formed, the temperature of the soil just under the surface is higher than that of the air just over it; (2) in which he inverted shallow metal trays over short grass and over soil; and (3) in which he weighed shallow pans of turf in contact with the ground, before and after dew had formed – as a result of all these, he became convinced that the ground loses moisture by evaporation even while dew is forming; loses more by evaporation than it gains as dew. He felt justified in concluding that much of the moisture that appears as dew does really come from the ground.

As to the second point, by a series of observations and experiments, Aitken shows that 'dew' can form on the leaves of many plants before they cool to the dew point, and that this is actually transpired water. He noted that in a garden at night some plants were much wetter than others, and that the moisture on these appeared chiefly as drops on the edges of the leaves. Even parts of the same plant showed great differences, depending on how actively they were growing.

Aitken was at pains to state that he was not denying that dew collected from the atmosphere as well – the dew on the roof of a shed, for example, can have no other source – but only arguing that there is more than one source of dew.

Some years later, without reference to Aitken, R. Russell came

[53] Aitken, 'On Dew.' *Trans. Roy. Soc. Edinb.* 33 (1885–6), 9–64. (*Collected works*, 134–86.)

to very similar conclusions from experiments and observations of the same general sort.[54] With this amendment to Wells's theory we may conveniently leave the subject. I have not mentioned nearly all the relevant literature; but I have tried to set out the main vicissitudes of the theory of dew.

[54] R. Russell, *Nature* 47 (1892), 210–13.

Chapter Ten

THEORIES OF HAIL

Antony: Cold-hearted toward me?
Cleopatra: Ah! dear, if I be so,
From my cold heart let heaven engender hail.

Shakespeare, ANTONY AND CLEOPATRA,
Act IV, xi, 157–59.

Of all the hydrometeors hail is at once the most spectacular and the most difficult to account for. It is therefore not surprising that the attempts to explain it have been very numerous, nor that many of them have been extremely far-fetched; and the task of the historian is largely one of selection, at least for the purposes of a book such as this.[1] One criterion that I shall adopt is that of novelty, rejecting all re-statements of ideas already discredited or superseded. Even then it will be necessary to be brief, and it is hoped that the citations will provide an acceptable substitute for a fuller treatment.

It will avoid misunderstanding if the term 'hail' is properly defined at the outset. There are four kinds of hail:

(1) *Hail* proper: Balls or stones of ice (*hailstones*). They may be made of clear ice or of alternate clear and opaque layers, and they may range in diameter from, say, 3 to 30 mm. or even larger.

(2) *Soft hail*, also called *Graupel, grésil,* or *snow pellets:* White, opaque pellets less than about 6 mm. in diameter, consisting of a central crystal of ice covered with frozen cloud droplets. They are relatively light and soft.

(3) *Small hail:* Essentially a nucleus of soft hail surrounded by a thin layer of ice.

[1] It may be worth recording that 90 years ago C. Wähner (*Historisch-kritisch Uebersicht über die Hageltheorien* [etc.], Rotterdam, 1876) took 90 large quarto pages to treat the subject to his satisfaction.

(4) *Ice pellets* (called *sleet* in North America): Transparent spheres of ice about the size of raindrops, which may have liquid water inside.

These various hydrometeors have a different origin and a different temporal and geographical distribution; for instance, the last three are predominantly winter phenomena, while hail proper seldom falls in winter – a puzzling fact which early theories had great trouble in accounting for. Again, hail is seldom found at a great height on mountains, while snow pellets are a familiar phenomenon there. In what follows, the word *hail* will be taken to mean hailstones, the phenomenon associated with summer and usually with thunderstorms.

It may be well to draw attention at this point to the two most difficult problems that had to be dealt with by the framers of theories of hail. These were, first, how is the great cold produced, to freeze the hailstones; and second, how do the growing hailstones stay in the air long enough for so much water to freeze on to them? The first problem became very much more difficult after the discovery of the latent heat of fusion in the last half of the eighteenth century, and took the form: how does the growing hailstone get rid of the heat of fusion of the water it collects?

The perceptive reader who has read Chapter eight will probably have guessed that the answer to the first question lies in the lapse of temperature produced by convective equilibrium, together with the great height of convective cloud systems. He may even have suspected that there may be vertical currents rapid enough to hold a hailstone aloft until it can grow to the size they sometimes attain. It may help the reader to understand the historical development, if he is told at once that this is so, that it is now quite certain that a hailstone loses heat mainly by conduction and by evaporation from its surface, and that these losses are quantitatively sufficient.[2]

The speculations of the ancients on this subject have already been referred to in Chapter one, so that we may begin with Descartes, who noted that hailstones often have snow in the middle, and speculated

[2] I hesitated to provide the reader with 'hindsight' in this way, until I reflected that I should be sorry if this chapter were clear only to those who had made a study of 'cloud physics.'

that large ones are formed because the winds have driven numerous snowflakes together, which have then been partly thawed and again frozen. The reason that large hailstones occur only in summer is that in winter the clouds are too low to give time for this thawing and freezing.[3]

This can scarcely have satisfied Descartes. Something more definite was provided by Gassendi, who held that the upper regions of the air are cold, not because they are far from the heat reflected from the earth, but because of the 'nitrous corpuscles' or 'seeds' of cold that abound there. These are fewer in winter and generate only snow, but more abundant in summer, so that hail can be produced.[4] The idea of 'nitrous salts' or 'nitre' to produce cold was even more popular after the writings of John Mayow,[5] and in 1697 we find the venerable John Wallis communicating to the editor of the *Philosophical Transactions* a 'letter concerning the generation of hail, and of thunder and lightning and the effects thereof'.[6] There was a fairly prevalent idea at the time that a flash of lightning and an explosion of gunpowder were, if not the same thing, closely allied; so John Wallis reasons that if nitre is in the air to produce lightning, it probably forms a freezing mixture with the snow, which freezes hailstones.

> And the rather, because (not only in those prodigiously great, but in common hail-stones) there seems somewhat like snow rather than ice, in the midst of them.[7]

Musschenbroek developed this chemistry further; after noting the common association of hail with lightning, he has the latter composed of oleaginous and sulphureous matter, as well as 'spirit of nitre, which, meeting the particles that form ice, excite a horrible cold . . .'[8] These 'particles that form ice' are essential, otherwise we get only heavy rain. It was a common belief, probably stemming

---

[3] Descartes, *Oeuvres*, Ed. Ch. Adam & Paul Tannery, 12 vol. + index, Paris, 1896–1911. Vol. 6 (1902), pp. 293–5.

[4] Pierre Gassendi, *Opera omnia in sex tomos divisas*. Leiden, 1658, Vol. II, p. 70.

[5] *Cf.* p. 73 above.   [6] *Phil. Trans.* 19 (1697), 653–8.   [7] *Ibid.*, p. 657.

[8] P. Van Musschenbroek, *Essai de physique* [etc.], tr. P. Massuet, Leyden 1739, p. 803.

from unrecognized observations of supercooling, that mere loss of heat is not enough to freeze water, but that it freezes

> because there become mixed with the water certain very slender corpuscles that come from our atmosphere, and produce a sort of fermentation with the water, drive away the heat (*le feu*) that is in it, and make its particles adhere to one-another.[9]

This appeal to the nitrous particles became less common as the eighteenth century progressed.

So some other source of the cold had to be found. It must have been generally observed that the clouds from which hail falls attain a prodigious height. At any rate Edward Barlow decided in 1715 that hail is a summer phenomenon because at that season

> heat abounds, to raise their vapours to a competent height; and so seldom in winter, or frosty weather, for want of moisture to cement 'em together, as well as of heat to raise 'em.[10]

J. A. Deluc, in the days before he turned to chemical speculations, wrote that the formation of hail is a proof of the great vertical extent of vapour. He believed that the central snowy core of a hailstone indicates that a snowflake has been formed at such a height that it will freeze round it the vapour it meets in its fall.[11] Similar views were expressed by Franklin[12] and by Monge,[13] but the latter would have drops, rather than vapour, collected. In the nineteenth century it was a tacit assumption of most writers that part of the process, at least, takes place at a great height.

A suggestion that seems in advance of its time was that of M. Saalfeld, who in 1763 devoted eighteen pages[14] to his reasons for thinking that 'all white clouds are frozen', and suggested that this can provide the nuclei for hailstones.

The celebrated experiment with the kite, showing the electrical

[9] *Ibid.*, p. 443.   [10] *Meteorological essays* [etc.]. London, 1715, p. 46.

[11] Deluc, *Recherches sur les modifications de l'atmosphère.* 2 vols. Geneva, 1772, ¶ 714.

[12] Franklin, *Mem. Manchester Lit. & Phil. Soc.*, ser. 2, 2 (1789), 373–4. This was read to the Society on 22 Dec. 1784.

[13] Gaspard Monge, *Ann. de Chim.* 5 (1790), 51.

[14] Saalfeld, 'Alle weisse Wolken sind gefroren.' *Acad. electoralis moguntina scientiarum utilium qua Erfurti est, Ubersetzungen und deutsche Abh.* 2 [1763], 100–17.

nature of lightning, was made by Franklin in June 1752. This led, of course, to a number of attempts to explain hail by an appeal to electrical phenomena. The fact that hail is very often, in fact usually, accompanied by lightning made this inevitable. The able chemist Guyton de Morveau fell into this logical trap.[15] Dismissing all ideas of 'salts' to produce a freezing mixture – why do we not find them in hailstones? – Guyton is constrained to look for an electrical explanation of the great cold that he feels must be needed. Accepting Nollet's finding that water evaporates more quickly when electrified,[16] he reasons that this should increase the cold somewhat, and he speculates that vapour may become a better conductor of heat when it is electrified. He supported his ideas by some very badly-controlled experiments.

Guyton was at once criticised by Jean André Mongèz in an open letter,[17] admitting that electricity increases evaporation, but objecting that electrified drops ought to repel each-other, not coalesce to form large hailstones. Mongèz had an elaborate theory of his own, quite unsupported by observation.

By the time he came to write his *Idées sur la Météorologie*, Deluc had quite abandoned his earlier theories about hail. He seems to have had two theories of hail by 1786, not necessarily mutually exclusive. The first was that the cold required must be chemical in origin,[18] and we have seen in Chapter six how much he relied on chemical analogies in meteorology. The second, electrical theory was based on the hypothesis that heat is produced when the 'electric fluid' is decomposed,[19] so that presumably the production of electric fluid must be accompanied by the absorption of heat. Deluc does not seem to make much of this, but Wähner[20] names Lampadius and Heidmann as having supported him. His chemical theory obtained the powerful support of Lichtenberg's literary talent.[21] 'Nobody,' wrote Lichtenberg,

[15] *Obs. sur le Phys.* 9 (1777), 60–67.
[16] See p. 42 above. This idea was, of course, later demolished.
[17] *Obs. sur la Phys.* 12 (1778), 202–11.
[18] Deluc, *Idées sur la météorologie*. London 1786, ¶ 642.
[19] *Ibid.*, ¶ 525.   [20] *Uebersicht über die Hageltheorien*, p. 31.
[21] See *G. C. Lichtenbergs vermischte Schriften*. Göttingen, 1804, vol. 3, pp. 85–133.

doubts that thunderstorms and hailstorms and the like are chemical processes in the great ocean of air, with decompositions and recombinations that must follow one another unceasingly.[22]

It ought not to be thought more astonishing that cold hail can be formed in hot summer weather 'than that a flame can burn on a cold day and produce 1,000 degrees of heat. The flame produces heat by ... decomposition; cold must be produced by recombination.'[23]

The most celebrated electrical theory of hail was that of another great physicist who was also an elegant and powerful writer, Alessandro Volta.[24] In this theory, electricity was used, not as a primary means of producing cold, but to explain the suspension of hailstones long enough to grow. The cold, thought Volta, must come from a very rapid evaporation from the tops of clouds, produced by the bright sunshine, the thin, dry air, the ease of evaporating the vesicles of which he thought clouds were made,[25] and the supposed effect of electricity in aiding evaporation.[26] But how are the hailstones kept in the air for a sufficient time? 'We cannot imagine any other force or power than electricity; it remains to see whether this can be adequate.'[27] Volta supposes that the hailstones bounce up and down above the top of the cloud by electrical repulsion, their charge being renewed when they re-enter the cloud after becoming a little heavier. Finally, their weight gets too much for the available electricity, and they fall through the cloud and out. An even more likely supposition is to have two clouds one above the other, oppositely electrified; for the charged hailstones will then bounce between them, like the pith balls between the plates in the well-known laboratory experiment.

Volta supports this theory by reference to the variety of the forms of hailstones, and to the fact that they have a little snowy mass in

[22] *Ibid.*, p. 89.

[23] *Ibid.*, p. 104. It was thought before the 'chemical revolution' that the air and the fuel decomposed one-another.

[24] Volta, 'Memoria sopra la grandine.' *Giornale de Fisica, Pavia* 1 (1808), 31–45; 129–39; 179–98.

[25] See Chapter 3 above.

[26] This idea had been exploded by M. Van Marum in 1799 (*Ann. der Phys.* 1, 112–22.)

[27] Volta (1808), p. 39.

the centre. He answers various objections: for example, why do not the oppositely electrified layers of cloud rush together? They will come together, but only slowly. And why are there not hailstorms in winter? Because the clouds are less dense, and hence less strongly electrified; the sun is less strong; and the long nights allow the re-establishment of electrical equilibrium.

This paper was so brilliantly written, and with such a wealth of detail, that it is not surprising that it gained wide acceptance, especially in view of the eminence of its author. The great Arago seems to have been convinced of the truth of Volta's theory, even in 1828,[28] after it had been subjected to a good deal of criticism, especially in Germanic countries. The first critic seems to have been J. J. Prechtl of Vienna, who refused to believe that the evaporation of water could produce such cold, especially in sunshine.[29] Prechtl also objected to treating clouds as if they were metal plates off which objects can actually bounce, and pointed out that the supposed repulsion of the upper cloud would be added to the effect of gravity and would produce an enormous downward speed.

What was really needed were some calculations, and this lack was partly supplied by G. W. Muncke about 1830,[30] who found that with any reasonable dimensions the possible repulsive forces would be entirely inadequate.

Not all the criticism came from north of the Alps. In 1817 Angelo Bellani[31] asked what, if a hailstone or even the nucleus of one could be repelled from the top of a cloud, would hinder the expulsion of the cloud droplets themselves? He also demolished by a beautifully simple experiment the idea that the bright sunshine in the upper air could help to engender the necessary cold. Two thermometers were covered with cloth and wetted; one was put in the sun, the other shaded. The one in the sun dried more quickly, but did not get cooler than the shaded one while it was drying.

Volta's theory of hail is one more example of the lack of success

[28] F. Arago, *Annuaire du Bureau des Longitudes*, 1828, pp. 188–97.
[29] I have not seen Prechtl's paper and am quoting Wähner (1876), p. 34.
[30] In *Gehler's physikalische Wörterbuch*, Vol. 5, *s.v.* 'Hagel'.
[31] Bellani, *Giornale di Fisica, Pavia* 10 (1817), 348–83.

with which even the most distinguished physicists of the time embarked on 'the ocean of air'. I leave it to the meteorologists to decide whether this merely indicates that meteorology is more difficult than physics. At any rate by the 1820s there had developed a general suspicion that the association of hail and lightning could mean no more than that both were produced in a similar weather situation. This was clearly the belief of Von Buch in 1814[32] and was stated flatly by Denison Olmsted of Yale in 1830.[33] From this time on, theories of hail were mechanical, and based more-or-less firmly on the ideas of rising currents of air.

For this we can go back to 1780 and Marcellin Ducarla-Bonifas, known as Du Carla, who had a theory of hail in his *Histoire naturelle du monde*.[34] A column of air, much more strongly heated than the surrounding atmosphere, rises violently enough to carry up its condensation products to a height where they freeze in the great cold into

> little snowy globules, which will grow until, their surface diminishing relative to their volume, they . . . fall back, very slowly at first.[35]

Indeed, they might 'remain suspended for several hours', in spite of their weight, by the violence of the ascending current. When they begin to fall:

> On their way they meet the aqueous molecules, coagulated by secretion and cold,[36] coming up towards them. These join themselves to them, spread out, and freeze; and balls of ice are the result, rounded both in their formation itself, and by rubbing together.[37]

If the vertical speed is great enough the raindrops can freeze together directly, and Du Carla thought that this explained the shape of some hailstones, which he described as a paraboloid stuck to a little sphere.

[32] Leopold von Buch, *Abh. Akad. Berlin* (1814–15), 74–75.
[33] Olmsted, *Amer. J. Sci.* 18 (1830), 1–11.
[34] Geneva, 1780. *Septième cahier*, 'Des météores locaux', pp. 92–97.
[35] *Ibid.*, p. 94.
[36] *Par la sécrétion et le froid.* The term *sécrétion* may be a reference to the idea of Nollet (see p. 173 above) that the 'vapours' seen in the receiver of an air pump are really impurities in the air.
[37] Du Carla (1780), p. 94.

This theory of hail depended on differences of surface temperature between different parts of the terrain, and Du Carla was easily able to explain why hail occurs mostly in summer, in the afternoons, and in country with a varied surface. It was, of course, an incomplete theory in that it did not consider how the latent heat of fusion is to be got rid of; the importance of this probably did not occur to Du Carla, if indeed he was aware that there is such a thing as latent heat.

At any rate, his book seems to have been little known outside of Geneva, and others rediscovered the fundamental idea of the rising current of air.

The peculiar geographical distribution of hail was an important clue. In 1795 M. A. D'Onofrio of Naples, in a work not otherwise of much value,[38] wrote about a hillside in the Kingdom of Naples that never had hail while it was covered with forest, but was subject to frequent hailstorms after it was put under cultivation.

D'Onofrio thought that this was because the trees had acted as lightning-rods, but Leopold von Buch had a better idea in 1814,[39] namely that the bare hillside, which faced towards the south-east, got much warmer than the forest had done, and that this led to stronger ascending currents.

There was certainly a connexion between the incidence of hail and the topography. Von Buch quotes Alpine proverbs such as 'where there are cretins it never hails', and 'where goitre occurs frequently, it hails seldom'. It is of course absurd to assume a direct causal connection, but there may be a correlation through the peculiarities of topography and the resulting water supply.

Von Buch has a theory of hail that is of much interest. From the observed shapes and structure of hailstones he deduces (as did Du Carla) that a snowflake has collected water drops, which have frozen to it. Thus it is a necessary condition that the upper layers of the air should be below freezing point, the lower ones above it. This is why there is no hail in winter. Graupel is the first stage of hail, but in winter it cannot develop by collecting raindrops. Von Buch

---

[38] D'Onofrio, *Meteorologische Abhandlung vom Hagel.* Dresden, 1795.
[39] *Abh. Akad. Berlin* (1814–15), 93.

considers that evaporation from the falling drop is sufficient to produce the cold that freezes it, and deduces that the largest hailstones occur when there is the greatest difference of temperature between the lower and the upper air. From some observations on and near various mountains, in which rain fell on the mountainside, hail in the valley, he concludes that hailstones grow large in the last 1,200 feet above the ground.

Von Buch acknowledges his debt to Du Carla for many of these ideas. In fact, the most prominent difference between their theories is that Von Buch, who knew about latent heat, had to find a way of abstracting heat from the growing hailstone, while Du Carla, who did not, felt no such necessity. Von Buch seems to have been impressed with the possibility of the growing hailstones being held aloft for a long time, and in this he either misinterpreted Du Carla or felt he was improving on him, for it is clear that the earlier author intended only that the ice nuclei should be suspended for several hours.

It is interesting that Von Buch says that hailstorms and thunderstorms often cool the whole atmosphere for days, 'as they bring down to earth the temperatures of very great heights, apart from the cold produced in the lower layers by evaporation'.[40] The explanation of this phenomenon is to be found, as we now recognize, in the formation of such storms at a cold front, particularly one that is invading a warm air mass of long standing. In fact, Von Buch simply got the cart before the horse.

He rendered a further service to meteorology by giving a measured temperature gradient near the ground as evidence of the ascent of heated air. In Geneva a thermometer, shielded from the sun, had registered 40° three inches over the grass and only 24° at three feet.

The theory of Muncke[41] is somewhat like those we have just been considering, but he put more emphasis on evaporation from the soil, combined with the lightness of water vapour, in producing vertical currents. All this vapour goes with the currents to great heights, where the surrounding atmosphere is far below freezing point. While the air that has risen can gradually cool off, it remains

[40] *Ibid.*, p. 86.
[41] *Gehler's physikalisches Wörterbuch*, Vol. 5, Leipzig, 1829, *s.v.* 'Hagel'.

warmer than its surroundings, but eventually haze and thin cloud will be formed. Muncke would not believe that air must cool on rising, because, evidently misled by what we should now call cold fronts, he was sure that the inverse phenomenon, the warming of sinking air, did not occur.

The next stage of the process is the beginning of massive condensation at great heights, with the result, according to Muncke, that the volume of the air aloft is diminished by that of the amount of vapour condensed, so that colder air from still farther up rushes into the space thus left vacant. In this some of the supercooled droplets resulting from the condensation are quickly frozen, and the ice crystals collect more droplets and form snow pellets which act as nuclei for the hailstones.

This further condensation produces a further partial vacuum, and the upper layers of air sink, the lower rise. This can cause the falling snow pellets to be carried up again. Air of course rushes in from all sides as well, which is taken to explain the rapidly varying winds near a hailstorm. Finally the hailstones become big enough to fall out, aided by the cold descending wind. Evaporation is relied on to get rid of the latent heat of fusion.

Muncke's theory, which was farther from the truth than those of Du Carla and Von Buch, seems to have got a good deal of attention in Germany and not much anywhere else, probably because Gehler's big dictionary of physics was read very little outside of Germany.

At about the same time, Olmsted published what we might now call a frontal theory of hail.[42] According to him, hailstorms are caused by 'the congelation of the watery vapour of a body of warm and humid air, by its suddenly mixing with an exceedingly cold wind, in the higher regions of the atmosphere'. The hailstones, of course, would grow by accretion as they fall through the warm humid air. A fair criticism of this theory is made by Wähner[43] when he says that it is possible that some hailstorms may be produced in this way, but not very often. But it is interesting that what was then thought to demolish Olmsted's theory was that hailstorms often

[42] D. Olmsted, *Amer. J. Sci.* 18 (1830), 1–11.   [43] Wähner (1876), p. 53.

affect a long strip of country running from roughly south-west to north-east.

Readers who remember the discussion of Espy's work in Chapter eight will not be surprised to learn that in his over-estimation of the power of ascending air he had a simple theory of hail. He suggested, indeed, that ascending currents may be strong enough to

> carry up large drops of rain . . . far above the region of perpetual congelation and freeze them there, and then carry them off to the side of the ascending column and precipitate them in the form of hail.[44]

It seems surprising, but as far as I have been able to determine, nobody objected directly to Muncke's statement that the condensation of vapour produces a partial vacuum, though it is just possible that it was Muncke that Espy was referring to when he denied that this could happen.[45] But when in 1862 Karl Friedrich Mohr promulgated a theory incorporating the same idea, A. Krönig immediately pounced on it and showed by numerical examples that under atmospheric conditions the condensation of water vapour, instead of forming a partial vacuum, will increase the volume, or the pressure, because of the liberation of its latent heat of condensation.[46] A year later Théodor Reye gave an analytical demonstration of this.[47]

For decades there nevertheless remained a hard core of meteorologists who persisted in believing that cold air could come down from great heights and stay cold, in spite of all mathematical demonstrations to the contrary. The most eminent of these was H. A. E. A. Faye, who became Inspector-General of Higher Education in France, and continued to write on the subject almost until he died. Others were C. Schmid[48] and Daniel Colladon,[49] who both believed the cold air to be dragged down mechanically by heavy rain.

A factor that began to be prominent in theories of hail after the middle of the nineteenth century was the effect of the supercooling

[44] J. P. Espy, *Trans. Geol. Soc. Pennsylvania* 1 (1835), 344.
[45] See p. 156 above.
[46] Krönig, *Ann der Phys.* 123 (1864), 641–50.
[47] Reye, *Ann. der Phys.* 125 (1865), 618–23.
[48] Schmid, *Zeits. öster. Ges. Meteorol.* 13 (1878), 436–7.
[49] Colladon, *Arch. Sci. phys. et nat. Genève*, 3rd ser. 2 (1879), 5–47.

of cloud particles. As we saw in Chapter three,[50] H. B. de Saussure had observed, sometime before 1783, that these could remain un-frozen well below the normal freezing point of water. This had been forgotten, and was rediscovered in the nineteenth century, along with the observation that raindrops can also supercool, producing glazed frost when they strike terrestrial objects.[51] It was a short step to the realization that snow pellets, falling through a supercooled cloud, could collect a good deal of ice, and at the same time this reduced somewhat the urgency of the problem of disposing of the latent heat of fusion in the comparatively short time available. The first to take this step seems to have been Vogel,[52] who did not, however, develop a full theory of hail. This was attempted by Karl Nöllner of Ham-burg,[53] using the fact of supercooling, but introducing a strange idea of his own about the effect of low atmospheric pressure in producing supercooled raindrops at great heights, rather than depending on ice crystals as nuclei.

At about the same time, P. H. Maille published a better theory, which unfortunately attracted no attention.[54] Maille's idea is that snow-pellets, formed high in the atmosphere, fall through a region of supercooled droplets. But he went much further than this in 1853:

> ... and if, besides the nucleus, which is often snowy (*grésilleux*) in large hailstones, there exist several snowy layers separated by compact layers, this would seem to indicate several oscillations and a see-saw battle between the force of gravity and the contrary push of the ascending current.[55]

It would seem that Maille was well ahead of his time both in 1834 and 1853.

The importance of snow pellets in the rôle of nuclei was noted

[50] *Cf.* p. 51 above.   [51] *Cf.* Wähner (1876), p. 56–57.
[52] According to Wähner. I have not been able to identify the original paper.
[53] Nöllner, *Die Natur* 2 (1853), 313–5; 321–3; 365–7.
[54] Maille, *Nouvelle théorie des hydrométéores* [etc.], Paris, 1853. The essentials of this theory are contained in the manuscript referred to above on page 161, which dates from February 1834.
[55] *Nouvelle théorie*, p. 218. In the 1834 ms. he says that the ascending current 'must contribute powerfully to the growth of hailstones' (fol. 41, recto).

by De la Rive,[56] Dufour,[57] Renou,[58] and Colladon.[59] Meanwhile a spectacular confirmation of the existence of supercooled clouds was provided by the courageous balloon flight of Barral in 1850, through a cloud layer 12,000 feet thick.[60] In the region between 11,250 feet and 18,990 feet, with temperatures between $-0.5°C$. and $-10.5°C$., he found the cloud to be in the form of droplets, while higher up there were ice crystals.

The latent heat of fusion of ice is about 80 calories per gramme, and thus if the cloud droplets are supercooled less than 80°C., not all the water will be immediately frozen. As the supercooling in the atmosphere is only a few degrees, most of the water will, in fact, not freeze to the growing hailstone. Thus supercooling does not get rid of the necessity of some method of disposing of the surplus heat.

The famous engineer Osborne Reynolds, not seeing any way in which this could be done, believed that all large hailstones are formed by coalescence, smaller stones adhering to slightly larger ones by pressure-melting and regelation. He thought that this is indicated by the fact that many of them have the form of a cone with a rounded base.[61] In support of this he tried with some success to make models of hailstones by spraying plaster-of-paris powder on to a splinter of wood in an atmosphere of steam. The shapes he obtained were not unlike those of some large hailstones. He was unaware that as early as 1834 Maille had suggested a way in which such shapes might be produced:

> When a snowflake comes to be impregnated with liquid, which makes it into a hailstone, it ought mainly to be its front or lower part that the liquid moistens and makes compact. This portion thus becomes specifically heavier than the upper part, which is porous and so is ballasted (*lestée*), as one might say. However, this position may not be very stable, for it can be changed by meeting with other snowflakes or hailstones.[62]

[56] *Traité de l'électricité*. Paris 1854–8, III, 178. (Quoted by Dufour, *Arch. Sci. phys. et. nat.*, Genève, n.s. 11 (1861), 29.

[57] L. Dufour, *Arch. Sci. phys. et nat.*, Genève, n.s. 10 (1861), 346–71.

[58] E. Renou, *Comptes Rendus* 81 (1875), 506–7.

[59] Note 49.   [60] Wähner (1876), p. 61.

[61] Reynolds, *Proc. Manchester Lit. & Phil. Soc.* 16 (1877), 23–33.

[62] P. H. Maille, unpublished ms., 1834 (see p. 161 above), fol. 39ʳ.

By the end of the century, as was pointed out by W. Trabert,[63] the hail problem had resolved itself into two questions: to account for the shapes and structure of hailstones, and to find a mechanism for getting rid of the latent heat of fusion. It was fairly clear that hail was formed in strongly ascending currents, well above the level at which the freezing point is reached, though at that time there was little real evidence that the vertical speeds could be high enough to suspend fairly large hailstones. The necessary speeds at various heights were calculated in 1901 by Paul Schreiber of Chemnitz,[64] apparently as a result of reading Trabert's paper.

It is rather surprising, perhaps, that until even more recent times the most obvious means of disposing of the latent heat of fusion should have been missed – simple conduction, that is to say the communication of the heat of the growing hailstone to the air molecules striking it in the cold air above the freezing level. Ingenious and elaborate studies[65] have shown that conduction and evaporation, operating together in the active updrafts of a large convective cloud, are adequate both in kind and degree to produce the largest hailstones. Most of this knowledge has been obtained within the last twenty years.

[63] Trabert, *Meteorol. Zeits.* 16 (1899), 433–47.
[64] Schreiber, *Meteorol. Zeits.* 18 (1901), 58–70.
[65] See B. J. Mason, *The physics of clouds*, Oxford, 1957, Chap. 6.

Index

Abbe, Cleveland (1838–1916), 159–60
Aberdeen, 70
Academia Naturae Curiosorum, 74
Achard, F. C. (1753–1821): 114n;
  electrical theory of dew, 182, 185
Adam, Charles, and Paul Tannery,
  20n, 44n, 93n
Advection, 82–7
Aether, 4
Air: Aristotle's definition of, 6;
  viscosity of, 52–4; advection of,
  82–7; elasticity of, 88; composition
  of, 138; descent of, 205;
Air, ascent of: 163; cooling by, 120;
  von Buch on, 151, 203; Espy on,
  156–60; Maille on, 161–3; Péclet
  on, 161; Peslin on, 163–5
Airy, George Biddell (1801–92), 55,
  143
Aitken, John (1839–1919): 'dust'
  particles, 173–6; pocket dust-
  counter, 175; on dew, 192
Albert the Great (1193–1280): 16–17
  De passionibus aeris, 17
Alexandria, 10
Alps, weather of, 116, 147
Amontons, Guillaume (1663–1705),
  83
Amos, 2
Anaxagoras (500–426 B.C.), 8
Anaximander (610–ca. 547 B.C.), 9
Anaximenes (6th c. B.C.), 4
Annales de Chimie, 130

Annals of Philosophy, 139
Antiperistasis, 8n
Aquinas, Thomas (1227–ca. 1274), 16
Arabic science, 14
Arago, D. F. (1786–1853), 158, 161,
  191, 200
Aristophanes (ca. 450–ca. 388 B.C.), 1
Aristotelian revival, 16, 17
Aristotle (384–322 B.C.): 3–10 *passim*,
  14, 16, 23; his definition of air, 6;
  on the four elements, 6; on hail, 8;
  on rivers, 9–10; on wind, 9, 10, 13;
  and Christian doctrine, 17; on cloud
  droplets, 43; on raindrops, 97; on
  dew, 177
  Meteorologica, 6–9, 10, 17, 177
  On the heavens, 7
  Physics, 7
Asia Minor, 2
Assmann, Richard (1845–1918), 56
Astro-meteorology, 17
Atmosphere, height of, 82–3
Atomists, 9
Augusta, Illinois, 159
Augustine (354–430), 12, 13

Babinet, Jacques (1794–1872), 57, 158,
  163
Bache, Alexander Dallas (1806–67),
  169
Bacon, Francis (1561–1626), 18
  Historia ventorum, 18
Barbaret Denis, 30